Pages 141 + 142 missing
21/3/00
Beccy

Emmerdale

Emmerdale

Written and with original photography by

Piers Dudgeon

EBURY PRESS
LONDON

First published in 1996 by Ebury Press
in association with Pilot Promotions

1 3 5 7 9 10 8 6 4 2

Ebury Press
Random House, 20 Vauxhall Bridge Road,
London SW1V 2SA

Random House Australia (Pty) Limited
20 Alfred Street, Milsons Point, Sydney,
New South Wales 2061, Australia

Random House New Zealand Limited
18 Poland Road, Glenfield, Auckland 10, New Zealand

Random House South Africa (Pty) Limited
PO Box 337, Bergvlei, South Africa

Random House UK Limited Reg. No. 954009

A CIP catalogue record for this book is available
from the British Library

ISBN 0091812658

Typeset by J&L Composition Ltd, Filey, North Yorkshire
Originated & Printed by Tien Wah Press, Singapore

The author would like to thank Helen Dixon of the
Emmerdale Production Centre and Rose Wheatley of the
Yorkshire TV Stills Library for their invaluable
assistance.

Contents

The Fire of Change

The minutes before catastrophe can seem to whisper a foreboding barely perceived at the time. On the cold winter evening of December 30th, 1993, in the Yorkshire Dales village of Beckindale, tensions were running high. At Emmerdale Farm it ought to have been a joyous occasion. Annie Sugden, married for the second time and in her seventy-fourth year, was preparing for a flight to Spain with new husband Leonard Kempinski.

On the cold winter evening of December 30th, 1993, in the village of Beckindale, tensions were running high.

The Sugdens had farmed in Beckindale for more than 100 years, and for the past 21, since her first husband, Jacob, died, Annie had been an emotional anchor not only for her family but for the community at large. Her decision to wed again was the clearest sign in a restive firmament that nothing would ever be quite the same again.

Annie Sugden's decision to wed was the most self-interested decision she had ever made. It woke up those close to her that what they'd taken for granted for so long was no longer sure. Her sons, Jack and Joe, had convinced themselves they'd come to terms with it, but even as Annie's luggage was heaped on to the kitchen floor, they threatened to spoil what should have been a fond farewell.

It was a seemingly silly argument about access to the village over Skipdale Bridge, blocked by new water works. Annie rebuked them, moving swiftly to dampen down even the least upset to her departure, unaware how important the issue would soon become.

In the bedroom of Mill Cottage, overlooking the beck from which the village took its name, Kathy Tate was contemplating an equally big change. Should she start a new life with her boyfriend Josh, or mend her unhappy marriage to Chris, son of Frank Tate, the man who was seen by some to be pulling up by the roots this age-old farming community?

Behind the lace curtains of Nick Bates's cottage in Demdyke Row, Elizabeth Pollard grasped a sharper nettle with both hands. She would do more than end her marriage to Eric, she would see that at last her husband got what he deserved for his sneaky low-life ways – 'And hopefully that's a jail sentence . . . Don't underestimate how I feel about you,' Elizabeth screamed, 'You're evil, Eric, and I curse the day I ever met you.'

Back at the Sugdens' farm, even as Annie's luggage was packed into the car, tensions climbed again. This time it was an argument between Joe and his stepson, Mark, over the return of a vacuum cleaner which he'd borrowed. It was an argument so absurd that it looked like reason itself had been eclipsed by the shadow of fate. For, as Joe would discover, the least event can feed our destiny, and he'd carry the guilty remembrance of this spat to his grave.

In the Woolpack, the village pub, a happier sort of drama was all set to unfold. There was to be a Dickens of an evening, a costume event and a reading from the master storyteller by the Woolpack's genial landlord, Alan Turner. His purpose was to raise money to help Seth Armstrong beat the NHS queue for an operation. Yet even good intentions couldn't mask the tensions which hung so inexplicably in the air.

There's a Seth Armstrong in many a Dales village. In times past there were many more than one. Poacher turned gamekeeper, Seth was in tune with the rhythms of nature, his mischievous humour a clue to their non-uniform beat. He lived by intuition more than by reason, and he would survive the catastrophe. But this lovable eccentric also had an uncanny ability to infuriate those around him.

Someone said Seth was looking too well to need his operation, that he'd probably cooked up the appeal for a bit of extra beer money. Seth took offence. Turner insisted he apologise for some caustic remark. Seth refused and poured scorn on Turner's efforts to make his appeal worthwhile. When the publican angrily ordered him to leave, Seth delivered his response cryptically on theme, 'I will, and it is a far, far better thing I do than I've every done before. . .'

The tragic line first spoken by Sydney Carton in Dickens' *A Tale of Two Cities*, when Carton took Charles Darnay's place on the scaffold, might be expected to have raised a smile. But it didn't. On this night of tragedy – 200 years after the one Dickens described – perhaps it was just too ominous.

All of which brought the village of Beckindale to the point of no return, and how appropriate that the man whose destiny it was to play a central role among those who will survive, should lead us to the very flashpoint . . .

Seth Armstrong, lovable eccentric, with an uncanny ability to infuriate those around him.

Entrepreneur businessman Frank Tate watched and listened from his comfortable chair in the sitting room of Home Farm. But it wasn't the carol concert on the TV set in front of him which creased his craggy features in thought.

Suddenly more characteristically determined, Frank rose from his chair and moved to the sideboard, where he picked up a present and fingered it, before hiding it away furtively as his daughter Zoe, Beckindale's young vet, came in.

Zoe sensed something, but their conversation failed to reveal what was going on in Frank's mind. When she left, Frank picked up the prettily wrapped present again, made his way out of the house, and drove to the stables where he knew he would find his ex-wife, Kim.

On arrival, he cursed. In the light from the stables, he could see that Kim had other visitors, and he stayed out of sight in his car. Vic and Viv Windsor, the village postmasters, had dropped by with Kelly, Donna and Scott, after an outing to the pantomime at Kelthwaite. They'd come on the off-chance of seeing their favourite horse, Samson. Kim was happy to oblige, though secretly she'd rather someone had come to see her. It was not the time of year for an attractive woman to be without anyone. Her thoughts had been of Frank, unaware that just yards away he was sitting, wanting to be with her.

Frank watched Samson nosing the children across the yard to their obvious delight but to his increasing frustration, as he counted the minutes until Kim would be free. He looked away, picked up Kim's present beside him, and made a decision to drive away.

At that moment he heard an almighty roar, followed by a blinding flash and a blanket of searing heat as a huge fireball appeared above him and erupted across the yard, knocking the group off their feet and exploding into the stables beyond. The dreadful sound gave way to a ghastly whinnying from the horses trapped in the barn, and the awful tinder-box crackling of dry wood and straw.

Elsewhere Kathy's brother, Nick Bates, was running through the night after his friend, Archie Brooks. 'Archie! Archie!' Nick called, as he dashed through the dark. Then suddenly he stopped, aware of a strange noise. Was it a storm? Something wet was falling from the sky, but it wasn't rain.

Frank Tate sees the fireball rear above him.

As Nick looked up, the wetness stung his eyes. Then he caught sight of Archie, silhouetted against the horizon as a huge fireball raced across the sky towards him. Nick watched, appalled, as the fireball dropped directly on his friend, who struggled with it momentarily, trying to get it away from his face and hands, and then disappeared in a cloud of vapour.

In the Woolpack, the entertainment had reached its climax. Alan Turner was reading to a hushed audience, but their attention was wrapped not by any fictional suspense but by a real eeriness, an unnatural, ghostly sound which redoubled into a roar before a sudden great influx of air shattered the windows, firing jagged shards of glass across the bar and throwing people to the floor.

On the road to the airport Joe made conversation to ease the strained atmosphere – 'Did you pack the sunblock?' he asked his mother. But Annie was looking at a strange glow over the horizon in the direction of the farm. 'Joe, what's that?' she asked curiously. Then two words from Leonard – 'Look out!' injected pure terror into the car and Joe swerved to avoid the wheel of a huge passenger jet which was hurtling towards them before a rolling sheet of flame.

Right: Jack Sugden amidst the devastation at Emmerdale.

In the Beginning

That death is a beginning as well as an end was a lesson learned long ago by the Sugdens. The family first acquired the leasehold of Emmerdale Farm from the Miffield Estate as an expression of Lord Miffield's gratitude after one Josh Sugden had sacrificed his life for his son in the Crimea in the 1850s.

One hundred and twenty years later, on October 10th, 1972, Josh's great-grandson Jacob's death marked the beginning of a new era, which would transform Emmerdale completely.

The story of Beckindale since 1972 is a true reflection of changes which occurred in many Dales villages in the same span. With improved communications with the outside world has come a transformation of values and expectations, which have changed its culture faster than at any period in its past.

What was so extraordinary about Emmerdale Farm in the early 1970s was how little had changed over the previous 100 years. Indeed, life was still characterised by certain customs and practices which were centuries old. Within Jacob's memory the farm labourers had worked for bed, board and pocket money, and there were still no scheduled holidays. Everyone got what could be afforded in terms of money and leisure. Of course the farming was to some extent mechanised, but Emmerdale was still worked according to the age-old mixed pattern (crops, dairy and livestock) for the purpose of subsistence.

The Industrial Revolution of the 19th century provided the transport and engineering which made big profits from farming theoretically possible. But better transport also meant that Britain was no longer an island economy. For those farmers who failed to take advantage of the new world markets, it meant unwanted competition from abroad and a crash course in the agonies of poverty.

In the 1950s and '60s Jacob's plans to turn Emmerdale into a going concern were thwarted by lack of capital. As a tenant farmer on the Miffield Estate he was drawing the same wages (about £5 a week in 1950) as Annie's father, Sam Pearson, who was employed as a labourer on the same estate by George Verney, the then Squire of Beckindale.

It had been Jacob's proud boast to Annie, when he married her in 1945 and moved her and Sam from their tied cottage into Emmerdale, that he would make her 'the happiest woman in t' Dales'. But very

Farming at Emmerdale has not been so much practised as lived.

soon Jacob discovered that he needed capital to make the improvements necessary to compete, and as a tenant farmer he had no means of raising it.

At first, none of this had worried Annie, who attached value less to money and things than to the simple operations of the human spirit, which were reflected in the tranquil beauty of Wharfedale and the challenging sublimity of the moors above.

That is not to say that Annie was in any way sentimental. Living and working in the Dales was hard. It bred a toughness which outsiders could easily misread as hostility, but which was, in truth, a mark of self-sufficiency – Annie never wore her emotions on her sleeve.

This self-sufficiency and the Dalesman's pride in

The church of St Mary's at Beckindale, where Jacob Sugden was buried.

his own culture combined with geographical seclusion to create an impression of insularity. There was indeed little contact with the outside world. Newspapers came to Beckindale, but few took one regularly, except for Farmers Weekly. At Emmerdale there was no electricity, only oil lamps, and no radio until an evacuee introduced one for a short period during the war. Few people came to live in the village from outside, and right into the 1970s Emmerdale was without a telephone.

It would be wrong to conclude that all this amounted to some sort of rural idyll. For Jacob's failure to realise his dreams drove him into a spiral of depression and he sought solace not in Annie's wider vision but in a pint glass at the Woolpack. With disenchantment and a liking for drink came debt and, in 1972, Jacob's early death.

By that time the farm was home not only to Annie and Sam, but to her two sons Jack and Joe, daughter Peggy, and Matt Skilbeck, a farm labourer who had long been part of the family in Annie's eyes.

Matt had a way with the animals on the farm (a touch of magic with his prize ewes in particular), which reminded Annie of her father Sam. Annie loved Matt as a son, and Matt loved 'Ma', as he called her. He had a quiet, stable temperament which Annie would have liked to see in her own sons, a predilection that never caused friction with Joe and Jack because (if for no other reason) Matt, like generations of farm labourers before him, knew his proper place.

Four years before Jacob's death Matt honoured his espousal by the Sugdens in marriage to Peggy. It was, on the face of it, the perfect union. But Matt was fated never to find lasting happiness in marriage, and in all his attempts to do so – even with Peggy – there was ever the suspicion that no woman could understand Matt's strengths as Annie per-

Emmerdale Farm, where the Sugdens lived from the 1850s until 1993.

ceived them. For, utterly honest and without a hint of ambition, Matt was even then a man out of time.

The spectacle of Matt in unaccustomed suit applying for a job in the city in order to supplement his family finances is as sad a picture as that of the millions of farm workers who uprooted a hundred years earlier, lured to the manufacturing towns by the promise of riches, gained by a few. That Matt was saved their disillusionment was due, ironically, to a movement in the opposite direction.

The arrival in Beckindale of Henry Wilks, a successful industrialist from Bradford, and his attractive daughter Marian, coincided with Jacob's death. And when a romance was sprung between Marian and Jack, Henry was drawn into the family circle and gave it just the advice and financial support it needed.

Before long the freehold of Emmerdale had been purchased from the Miffield Estate and a limited company formed with Wilks, Annie, Jack, Joe, Matt, Peggy and Sam its shareholders. Sam immediately

Annie, Peggy, Joe and Matt in the kitchen at Emmerdale.

The arrival at Inglebrook of Henry Wilks and his attractive daughter, Marian, coincided with Jacob Sugden's death.

Matt Skilbeck (left) at the trials, which speak of a shared sixth sense between handler and dog.

sold his shares to Henry and bought himself a new suit, which he wore for the first time to the sheepdog trials in 1973, a key event in the Beckindale calendar.

The trials add a dimension of keen competition to a proud tradition born of practical necessity. The sheep penning skills of farmer and dog are essential on the hill farms of the Dales and have been passed down from generation to generation since time immemorial. But more, they celebrate a relationship between man and animal which speaks of a shared sixth sense, a very different relationship with nature to the one shortly to be proposed, a marriage of science and business adulterated by chemicals and the exploitation of its issue for profit.

Watching the Dalesman work his dog, we have an inkling of a unique, shared understanding, bred in the bone, but also of a rarely spoken kinship with nature which underscores the Dales culture and makes the difference between being a farmer and being in the farming business.

That the Beckindale trials on this particular day, in the Spring of 1973, played host to an event which would rock the natural rhythms of life in the village as never before, was a portent of how wide-ranging would be the effects of change as Beckindale began its overdue emergence into the 20th century.

Sharon was seventeen years old and reckoned to be the prettiest girl in Beckindale. But she was also bright enough to be aware that there was more to life than ever was on offer to her mother, Beryl, a second cousin to Annie Sugden. Sharon read about life outside the Dales in books and she saw it on television. Television, more than any other medium, was the channel which conveyed to isolated and secluded Dales people how different life was on the outside and could be for them.

Jim Latimer at home in Beryl Crossthwaite's kitchen before the terrible tragedy was discovered. The rape and murder of Beryl's daughter, Sharon, was the first inkling of the dark side of Beckindale's overdue emergence into the 20th century.

A telephone and television were among the first modern appliances to appear in Annie's kitchen in the 1970s. Sam was so set in his ways that he refused to answer the phone, even when he was the only person at home. Television brought change of a different sort. It informed and entertained at the flick of a switch and offered imaginative girls like Sharon new expectations at a time when questions about the purpose of life were uppermost.

Sharon loved her mother and had enjoyed evenings spent with a cup of cocoa and their sewing 'just chatting over the day's doings,' as Beryl would recall to Annie in the wake of the crime. But now that she had left school and was working at Simms Bookshop, she had grown restless. She began to dread falling into her mother's ways, which now seemed petty and unfulfilling. Such were the difficulties of making a living locally that Beryl's husband had to work away from home as a clerk in the building trade.

Sharon wanted something more, and she knew that she had the personality, looks and brains to achieve it. A decade or so earlier, her ambitions would have been unthinkable, so little movement was there in or out of the village. A decade later, prospects of work in the village were so few and houses would become so expensive to buy that whatever their ambition, many young people would want to leave.

Sharon was on the very cusp of change. With a mixture of envy and ignorance about what was going on inside her secretive and ambitious mind, even her closest girlfriends interpreted Sharon's sense of her own destiny as aloofness and called her 'stuck up'.

In some other restless souls, for whom there was less chance that their expectations of a better life would be realised, frustration led to bitterness. Sharon's attacker was one of these.

Gawping Jim Latimer was in a way himself a victim. Shortly before he committed his crime, the factory where he worked in Hotten (Beckindale's market town) had closed down. Whichever way he turned, nothing ever quite matched Jim's expectations, and it irked him that he couldn't have what he saw others getting.

At the ruined abbey, where he first lured Sharon after he followed her from the trials and came upon

Amos Brearly, landlord of the Woolpack with Annie in 1972. His bold proposal of marriage was firmly declined.

her dangling her feet in the beck, Jim justified his wanting a kiss by saying, 'What's in a kiss? I mean look at them on the telly. They do it all the time, don't they? And they don't stop at a kiss. They don't hang about.'

It had all started as harmless banter. 'Are you doing anything tonight, Sharon,' Jim shouted across the meadow to the three girls chatting by the rope rigged up by Joe to separate onlookers from the trials area. 'I'm free if you're easy!' Then, to the amusement of his cronies, Gary and Robin, Jim had boasted, 'I'll get that Sharon Crossthwaite.'

His mates knew she wouldn't come across. Jim and Sharon were miles farther apart than the safe distance which separated them at the sheepdog trials. But Spring was in the air and anything seemed possible, not only to Jim. Even confirmed bachelor Amos Brearly, landlord of the Woolpack, had taken what was for him the bold step of approaching Annie with a proposal of marriage.

Spurred on by village gossip about Annie since Henry had become involved with the Sugdens and by Chairman of Dale Breweries Sir Peter Cheverley's wish to develop the Woolpack along family lines,

Amos had stepped in.

Annie had declined, and so uncharacteristic had been Amos's proposal that now he regretted making it, and as he overheard more tittle-tattle in the beer tent about Annie, marriage, and his own need for a wife, he became convinced that she had made his confidential overtures public.

Amos was at his most engaging when blustering his way into and out of a situation conjured up by his fertile imagination, but his performance that day was but a sideline distraction to the growing unease in Sharon as Jim continued his taunts.

'Ooh,' Jim spluttered over his beer glass to his mates, 'they've got the eye on us.' It was enough to build the false confidence he'd need to make his approach when later Sharon and her friends made their way along the sun dappled footpath home to tea.

When the girls split up, leaving Sharon alone, Jim couldn't believe his luck and followed her to the beck, watching from the cover of a tree above as she came to the bank and removed first one shoe and then the other, peeling off her stockings and giving her feet to the cool of the crystal clear water.

'Who's there?' she asked, suddenly sensing his presence.

'It's only me,' Latimer replied, suppressing a daft giggle, 'Just looking. No law against that is there?'

She made for her shoes. He grabbed them, enjoying the tease. 'Give them me,' she pleaded, 'Come on, give 'em me,' and then moved away not wanting to be too close.

It was a tug of war Jim knew he would have to win, but first he wanted to involve her in it, in the way of the romantic encounters he had watched on the telly.

'Nice here isn't it? Quiet . . . huh, heh, hum,' he began, his demented laugh barely covering the fact that he had explored the full repertoire of his courting skills and alerting Sharon to the need to bring the episode to a finish.

She made a hasty move towards the shoes. Latimer, pleased that she was entering in on the game, laughed triumphantly, 'You'll have to move quicker than that,' he said, adding with a leer, 'I've always had my eye on you. You know that? Hm . . . now I've got you, haven't I? All to myself.'

'Are you going to give me my shoes?' she demanded.

'You've got nice legs,' he continued, enjoying the power he held over the girl and holding out Sharon's shoes over the beck. But Sharon would have none of it and made her way purposefully up the bank barefoot.

Latimer realised a concession was in order and threw her one shoe. Sharon stopped to put it on and he handed her the other, but before she could take it, he tossed it further on, and as she bent down to retrieve it he made his move, grabbing her ankle – 'You didn't think you'd get away that easily did ya?'

'Don't be stupid Jim,' she said, frightened by the physical contact, 'Let me go.'

'Remember the last time I had hold of you?' Latimer asked, pulling her down into the depths of his infatuation.

'You never had.'

Sharon, breathless now, was unsure how to react.

'Oh yes I did. Just like this as a matter of fact.' He

The trials were a proud tradition born of practical necessity in the hill farms of the Dales. But in the Spring of 1973, they played host to an event which would shock the community to its core.

had his arms round her slim waist. 'We were kids
then though. Comin' back is it?'

'No, I don't remember.'

'Oh, oh, ho, ho, you can tell 'em. We were playin' a
game and I were holdin' you like this. I always
remember 'cos your heart weren't half going. I could
feel it with me hand . . .'

'I've got to be getting back, Jim, me mum'll be
wondering.'

'Not with trials on. Everyone gets off at trials.'

'But Jim,' she pleaded, hopelessly aware that reason wouldn't work her way into his sympathy.

'I'll tell you what, let's go for a walk.'

She realised she had no option but to play for time.
'A walk, where?'

'The old abbey, it's quiet there . . .'

'And Gary and Robin?'

'Don't worry about them. They're useless. I don't
need them. You're not frightened of me are ya?'

'No of course not.' She searched desperately
inside herself for a plan. He seemed to be offering
a way back from the edge of violence. She must play
along.

'Why should I be frightened of you Jim?'

'Just thought you might . . .'

'No. You just startled me, grabbing me like that.'

Her tone was deliberately reassuring and he
wasn't holding her now. That was progress of a
sort. Frightened as she was, there was normality in
a walk to the abbey, and Sharon hung onto that and
kept biding her time until they came to the banks of
the River Wharfe in sight of the abbey, when she
realised that if she wanted to avoid becoming part of
its ruined history she would have to impress on Jim
that people would be concerned and soon come
looking.

'I ought to be getting back, Jim.'

'It's quiet, nobody ever comes up here.'

'Look, Jim . . .' she began again in earnest.

'What?'

'I promised Mum I'd be back.'

'What for?'

'Annie Sugden. You know, Emmerdale Farm? Well,
she always goes in on her t'trials. I promised Mum I
wouldn't miss her . . . She's Mum's cousin, second

*The River Wharfe, near the ruined abbey (top left) where Sharon
Crossthwaite was lured by Jim Latimer.*

Every year at the time of the trials Trash made it his business to be in Beckindale.

cousin, and her Peggy's expecting.'

'Uh. She's not coming round to your house to have it is she? Uh,' Jim scoffed at the stupidity of her excuse and they sat silently for a moment. Then suddenly he grabbed her again.

'Oh Jim!' she cried, as her hopes disappeared into the distance as fast as the uncaring waters of the Wharfe below.

'Let's have a chat, talk a bit.' Jim suggested calmly, but his approach seemed only to increase the inevitability of what was about to happen.

'Jim,' Sharon implored him.

'You may as well sit down. C'm on. There's no point in standing up all the time is there.' Then, when she stood there, frozen to the spot, he came on more strongly, 'I'd like you to sit down.'

Sharon did what she was told and Jim, seeing her compliance as a positive reaction, developed his aggressive theme, 'I've got strong arms, haven't I?'

It was then that he moved over to kiss her.

'Let me go Jim,' Sharon pleaded again, struggling as he forced himself upon her. But he persisted, driving himself to the brink of violence once more – 'I don't wanta 'urt ya. I don't . . .'

Every year at the time of the sheepdog trials, a creature rarely found roaming the countryside today, but once a feature of the Dales, made it his business to be in Beckindale. The creature, human enough in form but barely so in appearance or habits, might be glimpsed furtively ducking down behind an old dry stone wall in search of a bite to eat, perhaps a couple of eggs from a henhouse, or collecting spent bottles from around Amos's beer tent with the idea of cashing them in later at the Woolpack, or running off manically across the moors for no apparent reason other than that his persecuted mind had conjured the impression out of nowhere that he was being sought by the police. It was his abiding nightmare.

Trash, so named for his dischevelled appearance, hideous odour and unkempt dress, a dirty old ankle-length raincoat and a battered, leather strapped roll-pack slung over his shoulder, was a tramp, a knight of the road, but with little of the romance or dignity which that implied. His appearance on the hill above the abbey at the moment that Sharon's nightmare seemed to be realised, caught Jim's attention.

'Get off you old tag!' he shouted. But Trash, suspecting something unnatural was going on below, picked up some stones and threw them one after the other at the couple. Furious at being interrupted, Jim jumped up to chase him away and gave Sharon her chance. As she slipped in among the ruins of the abbey, Jim saw his mistake and followed her, shouting, 'Sharon! Oh come on. Look, I like ya. I just wanted a kiss, that's all.'

Sharon huddled down silently in her hiding place, held her breath and prayed for night's fall, Jim's words ricocheting off the uneven surface of the walls around her. She was safe for now. But alas time, as Sharon might have gleaned from its marks on the consecrated fabric of her hiding place, takes no side in the end.

The rape and strangulation of Sharon Crossthwaite in the abbey ruins and the subsequent furore caused by the Latimers' attempts to exonerate Jim were

the first visible cracks in the surface of life in the village.

The incident caused such upset and unrest in Beckindale that Joe Sugden was driven to comment, 'For the first time in my life, I looked down Beckindale

Sharon's hiding place, where she held her breath and prayed for nightfall.

High Street and felt there might be something ugly there.'

19

What Love Means

Emmerdale Farm Limited, the company formed with the advice and financial assistance of Henry Wilks in the wake of Jacob Sugden's death, settled more than the immediate future of the farm.

When Jacob died he left a will, which stipulated that his eldest son, Jack, should inherit Emmerdale. Nothing unusual about that except that Jack had not farmed at Emmerdale or indeed anywhere for the eight years leading up to his father's death. In fact Jacob had as good as disowned Jack when he had upped and left Beckindale in 1964, appalled that any son of his should choose an alternative way of life to farming.

Emmerdale. It was the end of an era, which had had its roots deep in the past.

Jack's choice had been driven by a talent unprecedented in the Sugden line and which Jacob saw as a complete waste of time. Jack wanted to become a writer. When he had gone, Jacob's pride prevented him from making peace with his eldest son and he never saw Jack again.

Jack's surprise return on the day of the funeral had thrown Annie into confusion. She was thrilled to have her son home. For her sake it couldn't have come at a better time. But she foresaw a possible problem with Joe over the will. Joe had worked the farm every day of his life since leaving school, had a moral right to Emmerdale and was clearly the more practised farmer, though Annie had grave doubts that he was mature enough yet to take full responsibility. To add to the difficulty Annie's father, Sam Pearson, backed Joe's claim.

With the biblical names of Jacob and Joseph to the fore and the return after eight years of Jack, the prodigal son, the scene seemed set for a round of filial hostility of Old Testament proportions. But Annie and Sam had no need to worry, and Joe had no need to enter upon a conspiracy to deprive his elder brother of his birthright. For Jack, as it turned out, was quite prepared to hand Emmerdale to Joe on a plate. What's more, Henry's business experience allayed Annie's fears about Joe not being up to managing the business.

Jack had been changed by his experiences away. He had moved in literary and publishing circles in London and Rome. He had written a bestselling book, called *The Field of Tares*, and had amassed what seemed to Joe like a small fortune. To begin with, some of what Jack had acquired from these experiences benefited Emmerdale in a very practical way. When Henry Wilks first arrived, before Annie had

The shareholders of Emmerdale Farm Ltd, with Jack's future wife, Pat Harker, and Henry Wilks's daughter, Marian.
Clockwise: Henry, Pat, Sam, Matt, Annie, Peggy, Joe, Marian and Jack.

drawn him into the fold, he came into conflict with the Sugdens, and Jack sorted him out.

Henry was a no-nonsense businessman who had made his pile in the wool and textile trade in Bradford, but he had taken early retirement with the intention of finding time to breathe from making money. He genuinely loved the countryside and was a keen bird watcher, which would help smooth his passage into life in Beckindale. But at first, the transition did not run smooth.

Access to Inglebrook, the house near Emmerdale to which he and his beautiful daughter Marian moved, would, Henry decided, be greatly improved if he were able to use an old public right of way, which happened to run right through the middle of the Sugdens' farm.

Understandably, Annie, with whom Henry broached the subject, was not immediately taken with the plan. But what inflamed the situation and made Annie show him the door, was the way Henry went about getting what he wanted. Henry was a man used to getting his own way and when Annie didn't immediately fall in line he foolishly invoked the law.

Tact was what had been required. The Sugdens had been at Emmerdale since the Crimean War. Henry was an incomer. He may have had the law on his side, but while that was enough to keep his employees and their unions in line at his Bradford factory, Annie didn't take kindly to being bullied into submission by it. The law, while often expedient, is not always fair, or even just, and by attempting to use it to overturn tradition for his personal advantage, Henry had not been wise.

An incomer called Thatcher would try something similar nearly a decade later and meet the might of the whole community of Beckindale. But this time it was the Sugdens battling alone, and when Henry briefed Peters, his solicitor in Hotten, it was Jack who brought his experience of the world to bear. Jack looked at the small print of the right of way order and discovered that the carriageway at the centre of the dispute followed an even older path, which continued beyond the farm onto Inglebrook's land.

The footpath past Inglebrook had fallen into disuse because of mud, Jack informed them. Perhaps Henry would like to perform a similarly

Incomer Henry Wilks, pictured with his solicitor, Peters, brought the Law into a quarrel which clouded his first dealings with the Sugdens. But Jack saw them off and the old order prevailed.

public spirited act and drain the land to allow public access to his property, which, incidentally, would take ramblers right past his drawing room window!

Jack's victory was born of his experience of sorting out the fine print in his publishing contracts. But protecting his own interests had been second nature to Jack for some time. In this case they coincided with his family's interests, but his period abroad had confirmed and developed the trait along more self-centred lines.

Jack's philosophy of life was enshrined in the theme of his novel, *The Field of Tares*. On the face of it, the book was just another bestselling racy read. Baldly the plot told of a young man arriving in London and taking up with a girl. The affair went well and they lived together in the throes of first love. But the girl showed signs of becoming dependent on him and he shied away, falling for another, a beautiful, independent free thinker who demanded nothing more of Jack's hero than that he be himself and let her be herself.

When, at the suggestion of this girl the three of them lived together in a kind of *menage-a-trois*, his first love suffered badly in the arrangement (and would eventually be destroyed by it). Jack's hero became fraught with the tension between the moral code in which he had been reared (by which his duty was clearly to his first love) and having the nerve to free himself from convention and embrace a self-centred morality unconcerned with the fate of others.

This was London in the swinging sixties, its artistic roots in the '50s of John Osborne's 'Angry Young Man'. What Jack was exploring was the fashionable philosophy of existentialism, which gave individuals back a natural right to live life according to how they felt, irrespective of pressures to conform to the conventional, Christian ideal of duty to others.

There is irony in the novel's title, which is a quotation from a story in the New Testament, *Matthew* 13, verses 24-30. The story tells of a farmer whose enemy has sown tares, or weeds, into a field of wheat. The Lord tells him to 'let both grow until the harvest and in the time of harvest I will say to the reapers, "Gather ye together first the tares, and bind them in bundles to burn them: but gather the wheat into my barn"'

But Jack had no time for religion. His stirring arguments with Edward Ruskin, the vicar of Beckindale, make that clear. Jack believed that man should take responsibility for his own life and live independently of society which inflicts its own codes upon him. Jack's first commitment was to himself, as his relationships with girls in Beckindale showed – first with Pat Harker, then with Henry's daughter, Marian, and, shortly after Marian's subsequent departure for Italy, with Squire George Verney's wife, Laura.

Jack was attractive to women in both the worlds in which he moved because he was an outsider. In the world where the steamy relationships in his novel were lived out, he brought the primitive culture of the Dalesman. He had deeply ingrained in him Annie's sense of the value of nature, and money for its own sake was never a prime motive. (No doubt the glamorous women he met in London and Rome required that he had money, but his success as a writer had ensured that.)

One might expect that the women he wooed in Beckindale were attracted by the sensitivity which employed him as a writer. But if so, they must have been deeply disappointed. In 1964 he left Pat Harker in the lurch. She had become pregnant and Jack had left her when he left the village. On the rebound Pat married Tom Merrick, never telling him that her child was not his.

Jack with Pat Harker. In 1964 Jack had left Pat in the lurch and she had brought up their son, Jackie, telling her husband Tom Merrick that the boy was his.

Eight years later, on his return to Beckindale, Jack took up with Henry Wilks's daughter, Marian, and again found himself unable to make a commitment. True to his code, he told her that there was no need for promises, no need for meaningless contracts, 'It's what is felt that counts.'

'I'll tell you something,' Marian said, 'you don't understand, you won't understand – because you are always thinking about yourself.'

Then, Jack's affair with London-loving Laura Verney, errant wife of George Verney, reduced the Squire of Beckindale to a laughing stock in his own village and Jack so upset him that Verney horsewhipped him in the courtyard of the Woolpack.

It is tempting to dismiss Jack, as his brother did, as unbelievably insensitive. 'For a man who made a fortune out of a book about people,' Joe once told him, 'you know absolutely nowt about them.' But here was a man seriously looking inside himself for an answer to life at whatever cost. His commitment to living free may appear insensitive and selfish, but so be it if that is what it took to escape the suffocating conventions of life in the Dales, as Jack saw them.

It is certainly true that if Jack's girlfriends had been as honest as he, they would all three have admitted that they were attracted to him because they too were bent on escape of one sort or another. And at the very least, one has to admire the rigorous honesty of his approach. Jack was determined to sort out Henry Wilks because he had learned that effluent from Wilks's factory in Bradford had poisoned half the fish in the Tanet. And in the course of his affair with Laura Verney, when it would have served him to lie low, he didn't hesitate to call her husband to task when he heard that Verney was abusing his position of power.

George Verney was a major shareholder of Dale

When Jack falsely accused Squire Verney (above) of being instrumental in the eviction of Frank Blakey from the Forge, he took his punishment from Verney's whip without complaint.

Properties, a company in the process of evicting blacksmith Frank Blakey from the Beckindale Forge. Under the impression that George was behind the move because Blakey had refused to shoe the horses of the Verney hunt, Jack gave the story to the newspaper under the banner, 'Anti-Blood Sport Blacksmith Victimized by Landlord'.

Any other man engaged in cuckolding the village Squire might have ducked the issue, but to Jack, principle was all, and to give him his full due, when he discovered that Verney was not in fact to blame for Blakey's eviction he took his punishment at the end of Verney's horsewhip without even attempting to protect himself.

Jack was by this time something of a cultural schizophrenic. Not truly belonging anywhere, he had retreated from Emmerdale to the old mill house by the stream, which he recalled as a place of magic since boyhood. Confused by the contrary pulls in his life, and the chaos which appeared to follow his principled stands, he opted for peaceful isolation where he could write and live his life with no responsibility to anyone.

Jack (left) was an outsider even in the community of his birth, and he went to live alone in the mill house (right) before leaving Beckindale for the second time, in 1974.

The period coincided with the search for the body of Sharon Crossthwaite, and who should Jack find one day asleep on some old newspaper in front of the fire, but the dirty old tramp, Trash. In Jack's terms Trash was the true existentialist, a man (his real name was Ian MacIntyre) who had been a librarian, a pillar of conventional society, respectably married with a wife and daughter. Trash had taken the plunge, shed the shackles of society, and Jack befriended him, although interestingly he did first insist that Trash take a bath.

Then one day Trash gave Jack a watch which had belonged to Sharon. Jack knew that Trash had nothing to do with her disappearance and tried to get him to see that he must bury his paranoia about the police and report it to the village bobby, PC Ball. Jack couldn't see that Trash was sick, his paranoia not a philosophical weakness but a medical condition, and when he left him alone in the mill Trash jumped from a first floor window and broke his neck.

Even then, because his instincts are so good, it isn't easy to dismiss Jack for the fool that he plays. His mother, an artist in life rather than fiction, who saw into things and understood people like none other, worried more about Jack at this time than about anyone in the family. Annie could see where Jack was going wrong and knew that he would never come good until he left his ego behind and gave himself up to the natural rhythms of the farm. But she would not tell Jack what he must do. She realised he had to come to it on his own, as he surely would, albeit nearly a decade later.

Jack left Emmerdale for a second time in 1974, to write the film of The Field of Tares. The process of his disillusionment occurred over the next six years. When he returned, the ink in his pen had dried up. What had made it flow no longer mattered to him. All that mattered, he told his mother, was 'the flow of life in Beckindale. Why didn't I see it, Ma? Why didn't I see it was there, waiting to be written about?'

His father, Jacob, might have asked him, 'Why didn't you see that it was waiting to be lived?' Because by then it was too late. The flow of life in Beckindale had become more of a raging torrent, though Jack would do his utmost to stem the tide of change in farming practice.

Back in 1973, Jack Sugden was not the only man in the village fraught with anxiety. The Reverend Edward Ruskin, Beckindale's 54-year-old vicar, had been deeply involved in the distressing events surrounding Sharon Crossthwaite's murder and in counselling both Jack and George Verney. He had also acted as patron for a new face in the village, one Alison Gibbons, who (unknown to anyone else) had a police record for shoplifting. Alison had been courted first by Amos – still desperate to satisfy his brewery's preference for married publicans – and then by Henry Wilks. Alison liked Henry but couldn't bring herself to tell the truth about herself, which she regarded as essential to a lasting relationship. Ruskin was caught in the middle of it all, and he criticised himself for his failure to help George and Laura Verney with their marriage problems before Jack had become involved, to spot the devil in Jim Latimer before it was too late, and to help Trash before he committed suicide.

The one bright star in Ruskin's firmament was over Emmerdale, where Matt's Peggy had returned from hospital with twins, Sam and Sally, their birth perfectly timed to translate the tragedy of the discovery of Sharon's body into a promise of hope for the future. The Skilbecks had moved into Hawthorn Cottage on land which Emmerdale Farm had added to its assets when its owner, Jameson, had put it up for sale.

Ruskin was a country vicar of the old school. He took his mission seriously, which meant his own personal failures too. But the reason he tortured himself so was the direct result of his sessions with Jack. He had identified Jack's quest as a spiritual one not unlike his own. Jack had even admitted to Ruskin that he would love to have faith in Ruskin's God but couldn't see how he could commit himself to a code so obviously at odds with what went on in the world. So compelling had Ruskin found Jack's honest self-assessment that it raised doubts in Ruskin's own mind about his faith.

Against this background, Peggy fell ill and died from a brain tumour. The suddenness of her death took everyone at Emmerdale bad, especially Matt and Annie. But when Joe asked Ruskin to come up to Emmerdale to comfort Annie, the occasion turned into a battleground for the forces claiming the moral high ground in Beckindale.

The Reverend Edward Ruskin with his wife and Alison Gibbons (seated) in the vicarage drawing room.

'Comfort?' Jack exclaimed when he learned Ruskin's purpose, 'How can anything be a comfort at a time like this? Though no doubt you'll find some soothing syrup to pour out on us. Go on, let's hear it. Account for it all. Show us how good and loving your God is, when He can do a thing like this.'

Ruskin talked to them about the nature of God's purpose, His overall strategy in which individual events cannot be expected always to make sense.

Jack then listed the recent tragedies, Sharon's murder, Trash's suicide, and now Peggy's death from a cerebral haemorrhage – 'Purpose? What purpose can there be in it? Only an idiot can believe there's a purpose.' Jack would not let go until Joe forcibly removed him from the room and told him to leave Ruskin alone – at least Ruskin was trying to build something up, 'But all you do is tear things down!' he shouted.

Jack might have replied that things needed tearing down in places like Beckindale before anything could be built up. But he didn't because Trash's death had really got through to Jack, and deep down he was already distancing himself from the cauldron of restless emotions in which his writing was brewed.

Both Jack and Ruskin were dissatisfied souls. In the end only Annie's response to the situation made any sense. Rather than seeking a logic in the unexplainable, she brought the argument to an end by turning away from them to feed Peggy's twins.

Christianity had set the moral tone in Beckindale for centuries. Ruskin's doubts marked the beginning of decline in the influence of the Church in the village over the following years, and Jack's new code was the first sign that people would in the future feel free to put themselves first and follow their own feelings and convictions rather than kowtow to convention. After Peggy's death came the question of the twins' christening, and Matt told Alison Gibbons that he felt hypocritical going through the ceremony when he could no longer believe in a God that would rob Peggy of life so unfairly.

'I don't fancy putting my kids through a ceremony that I don't set any store by,' he told her.

For Matt of all people, rural tradition and convention had been sacrosanct. Clearly surprised by his outburst, Alison pulled him firmly to ground, telling him that it would be selfish to go against convention 'just because you want your way'.

Matt conformed. His faith in God may have been shaken, but his faith in those around him and the traditions of life in the Dales, had not been, nor would it ever be, even though he too would leave eventually.

Few had better reason to persuade Matt than Alison. Both Amos, Henry Wilks and even Matt himself courted this gentle, honest and genuine soul. And all were amazed when they discovered her dark secret. But it was that same secret which inspired Alison to advise Matt, for she knew from bitter experience what it was like to live outside society.

Meanwhile Annie, with or without Jack or Ruskin or indeed Alison's experience of Her Majesty's prisons, managed somehow to resolve differences and transform the lives of those around her. With a deeper understanding of life than any of them she did not seek to judge or justify it, any more than she would the cycle of birth-life-and-death on the farm at Emmerdale, which she knew lay at the bottom of all things.

Whatever her son Jack or the vicar or anyone else might say or write, they would not loosen Annie's instinctual grasp, though there was one time when it was truly shaken.

A while after Peggy's death the twins were killed in a car crash with their Aunt Beattie. The news seized Matt like a devil by the throat. He ran from

Hawthorn Cottage, bought by Emmerdale Farm Ltd from Jameson in 1973, was first home to Matt and Peggy Skilbeck, then Joe lived there with his first wife, Christine, before selling it

in 1977. In 1993 Jack bought Hawthorn again and lives there today with his second wife, Sarah.

Matt and Peggy's twins were Annie's great joy.

the farm not knowing where, just that he had to escape the agony of its hold, returning exhausted and drained an hour before dawn to find Annie waiting for him in the kitchen. She didn't fog him with false hopes, she told Matt only what she knew for sure.

'Nowt that is given to us lasts for long. We love and then we lose – nothing stays the same. I loved Peggy, she were a daughter as pretty and bright as a primrose. And I loved the twins . . . I can't deny that losing them has brought my heart near to breaking point . . . But if I came to choosing, I'd rather have had the heartbreak of losing them than never have had the happiness they brought us in their little lives . . .

'I feel it deep inside me. We'll grieve, we'll always remember your lovely little ones, Matt – but we'll survive because of what they gave us, an understanding of what love really means.'

Only afterwards, when the twins had been buried and Matt was asleep in his room upstairs, did she collapse in her son Joe's arms and cry. It was the first time Joe had seen her draw strength from another, instead of giving it.

Talk in t'Village

The story of Joe Sugden's affair in 1976 and 1977 with Kathy Gimbel (or Davis, as she had become) was another milestone along the rocky road of change in Beckindale. It brought the devil to the surface of life and paraded him not as expected by Kathy's father in the guise of fornicator but as hypocrite and bible-thumper and vocal moralist.

The sexual revolution and all that it implied left many emotionally wounded and even dead in its trail. In Beckindale it led to the suicide of Kathy's father and to the disintegration of the Gimbel family. Wherever it took place, it had the propensity to split families and destroy traditional loyalties which helped bind communities together however imperfectly. But liberation also brought relief to many and was a force in the campaign by women for equal rights.

When Sam was outraged by what Joe and Kathy did, Annie would remind him that little Sarah Crutchleigh had broken her heart when she had become pregnant and been bundled out of the village by her parents. 'How she cried over that one lapse,' Annie recalled, 'We never saw her again, did we? . . . Now, these days, she'd be at home where she belonged, with her parents. And the babby'd have that much better start in life.'

Kathy Davis (née Gimbel), who set tongues wagging in Beckindale in 1977.

A decade later, when Sandie, the daughter of Tom and Pat Merrick, had conceived a baby with Andy Longthorn, she was advised by a doctor in Hotten, a specialist in the newly designated area of 'womens problems', that an abortion was her right. Dr Clare Shaw believed in the 'management of nature' (a phrase which meant something to farmers by that time). 'She don't go for the idea of unwanted babies,' Sandie explained to Andy, 'Says women shouldn't be slaves to a biological necessity.'

To the Longthorns, a family dedicated to the principle of fine stockbreeding in Friesian cows and as deeply entrenched in the culture of the Dales as Sam and Annie, this was out of the question. Andy must forego his place at university, they insisted, marry Sandie and provide for her by working the family farm, a course for which he was ill-suited.

But such had been the pace of change that by 1984 Sandie felt perfectly at ease neatly to sidestep the horns of her dilemma and announce to the startled throng, 'I'm going to lead my life my own way.' She promptly left for Aberdeen to live with her father, Tom.

Joe and Kathy's revolutionary decision to live together openly, unmarried, occurred mid-way between the cases of Sarah Crutchleigh and Sandie Merrick, and like so many changes in Beckindale in the 1970s, it was judged against the background of a 19th-century morality.

Jim Gimbel was an evangelical. He lived according to John Calvin's 'hard law of religion', a strict Protestant ethic. Jim believed in the terror of hell

Freda Gimbel, mourning the total absence of love at Holly Farm.

Jim Gimbel believed in the terror of hell and kept discipline at home with a leather belt.

and kept discipline at home with a leather belt.

Gimbel's regime was far from being unusual in the Dales. A year after the affair of Joe and Kathy, 16-year-old Pip Coulter would be driven out of the family home into the arms of Steve Hawker by the high temperature religious atmosphere generated by her mother, Pam. There was romance and optimism in the youngsters' flight to a derelict cottage, a brightness of life which neither had known before. But then Steve had decided they needed money to get wed and stole Joe's shotgun, which he used to hold up the Woolpack, and sadly the amusing spectacle of Amos and Henry being bundled into the cellars turned to tragedy as two young lives were ruined before they had properly begun.

Joe had known Kathy Gimbel all his life and was no stranger to her brother Martin, father Jim and mother Freda. Now there was a third child, Davey, and all lived at Holly Farm on land adjacent to Emmerdale. After leaving school Kathy had made a mistake with 'a bad lot', as Annie referred to Terry Davis. She became pregnant. Pressured by Jim, Kathy had done 'the right thing', married Terry and moved to Hotten. She had lost the baby mid-term and, by then sadly aware that her husband was about 'worth his weight in burnt straw', had deserted Terry and returned to Beckindale, about the time that Joe was busting up with his first wife, Christine.

Kathy's return in 1974 was not welcomed by her father, who redoubled his efforts to discipline his children. Freda meanwhile lived the life of duty which was expected of her and privately mourned the total absence of love at home.

Because of all these troubles, Jim Gimbel's barley was the last to be cut the year Kathy returned to Holly Farm, which meant that the Seeding Cut would be held on his land.

Rather appropriately, this ancient custom, a fertility rite, provided the opportunity for Joe and Kathy's reunion. Joe had been racing across Gimbel's land with the rest of the lads from the village in his effort to become Seeding King, but had fallen and hurt his ankle while attempting to overtake James Bonfils, a rival of his in more than the race. It was then that fate stepped in unexpectedly to find Joe his Queen.

Before long Kathy and Joe were finding consolation in each other's arms, Kathy for the misery of her life with Terry, Joe for the break-up of his marriage to Christine.

On the night of the Cut, much of which Kathy had been spent with Joe in Hawthorn Cottage (where he and Christine had lived after Peggy's death), she had been too scared to return home and had stayed until dawn in Mill Cottage, creeping back into Holly Farm before her father was up.

Of course Jim knew that she had been out. He thought Kathy was bad enough for deserting Terry, and he would do his damndest to ensure that she didn't just take up with men where she had left off before marrying him. But Kathy was not loose in Jim's sense, rather she was desperate for the comfort of normality. She could walk or go to the cinema with James Bonfils or be close to Joe, drawing

Amos and Henry being bundled into the cellars of the Woolpack by Steve Hawker during the robbery in 1978, another attempt by a young couple to escape a rigid and oppressive morality at home.

For Sam Pearson the good of the whole community came first, and he could not accept his grandson's action.

comfort from his special understanding of her situation with Terry, without trading their friendship for sex.

Unable to accept this, Jim Gimbel began making regular trips to the Woolpack, a place he abhorred, to find out where Kathy was. At first it was Bonfils he bad-mouthed publicly there, convinced that Kathy had spent the night with him following the Seeding Cut.

So diseased did the relationship become between father and daughter, and so rife the village gossip about it, that Jo forced himself to go up to Holly Farm and put Gimbel right. It took some courage to light the taper of a charge which Joe knew would explode in his own face once he had removed Bonfils from Gimbel's line of fire.

For Jim, a contract signed in the Church of God was all. Kathy's marriage contract with Terry, albeit signed with a shotgun levelled at her reputation, was in the end what counted, as was Joe's with Christine. When Joe arrived, Jim grabbed him by the coat and attacked him verbally, perhaps lacking the courage to do more. He then disowned Kathy – 'she's no daughter of mine!' – and cut off all communication with his neighbours at Emmerdale – 'I'll never speak to you or yours again as long as I live.'

Asked by Annie whether it had been a successful foray, Joe replied, 'We-ell . . . You couldn't say he's forming a Sugden family fan club.' But the longer term consequences of the visit were worse. When

sixteen of Emmerdale's sheep strayed through a broken section of one of Joe's drystone walls, he let it be known that they would not be returned until the Sugdens payed an amount which he, according to the law, had a right to assess.

At this stage, Annie stepped in. Freda met her at the door of Holly Farm, distressed to hear that Annie wanted a word with Jim because although they were fond friends, she knew that when Annie got involved, things tended to come to a head. Annie brushed her fears aside, telling Freda to go and busy herself in the barn and assuring her, 'This won't take long!'

Annie began by tackling Gimbel's blind subservience to religious principles. The Bible may be against adultery but, she challenged, '"Let him that is without sin among you, cast the first stone." Are you without sin, Jim?' Then she took him up on his forcing Kathy to marry Terry in the first place, and the lack of care for his daughter when she had lost the baby – 'a terrible thing for any woman, Jim'. Finally, she faced him with his public accusations of Bonfils and Gimbel's public revenge on Joe. 'Can you really look at yourself and say your pride isn't the cause of all this trouble?'

Annie knew something about a man's pride. Jacob's pride had led to nothing but sorrow. Before long Jim would throw his own son, Martin, out of Holly Farm for neglecting his work and, like Jacob, be unable to eat humble pie and ask him back.

Annie knew what she was dealing with in Jim Gimbel, and having had her say, she pulled back and offered him the space to find his own dignified way out. 'You've always been someone I looked up to,' she said. 'I've called you an "upright man", many a time. If you tell me that all you have is your pride . . . Jim, it would grieve me.'

It worked, at least for the time being. As Annie moved towards the door, she called back, 'I'll tell Joe, shall I? To come tomorrow for the sheep?'

'Aye . . .' was Jim's resigned response.

Meanwhile the friendship between Joe and Kathy developed, the gossips at the Woolpack serving only to bring them closer together. Then, quite suddenly, as if Kathy was overcome by her relationship with Joe being driven too fast by events on the outside she told him she was leaving for Hotten. Joe was bitterly disappointed. He felt they'd been beaten.

Demdyke Row, where Joe bought a cottage to live with Kathy.

Beckindale had won. 'The trouble with this place,' he once said, 'is that everybody thinks they can run your life for you!'

But this time Kathy's sojourn in Hotten, where she worked in a coffee bar and lived alone in a flat, was brought quickly to an end by Annie when the atmosphere at Holly Farm sent Freda Gimbel into decline. Annie suggested that Kathy come home to look after her mother, and the Gimbel girl arrived back in the village just as an attempted reconciliation with Joe and his wife, Christine, had failed and the couple separated for good.

As a direct result of the split, Joe had decided to sell Hawthorn Cottage. Later, he would explain to Kathy that 'nothing seemed to work out there, 'cept we had some nice times didn't we?' Even though it was a place where she and Joe had known happiness, Kathy could understand what Joe meant. Peggy had died there; Joe's marriage had failed there. Kathy had an extraordinary understanding of the spirit of place and how a house could be affected by what went on in it.

But the fact that Amos took delight in telling her about the sale on the day of her return pained her dreadfully because she could see that he was obviously enjoying reinventing the atmosphere of scandal in the Woolpack which had earlier attended their affair. Henry Wilks, appalled at Amos's lack of tact, admonished him at once, and when Amos objected, saying, 'I wasn't hinting at anything,' Kathy showed her metal – 'You couldn't hint,' she lashed out at him, 'You're about as subtle as a sledgehammer.' Clearly this time round Kathy meant business.

Amos's talent for busying himself with other people's business would soon be channelled in a more official direction. He would apply and be accepted as Beckindale correspondent for the Hotten Courier, following the death of Percy Edgar. Edgar's demise had another significant effect, it released his cottage in Demdyke Row onto the housing market.

There was no immediate passionate renewal of Joe and Kathy's affair. A little older, a lot wiser, they took up again on what seemed a more mature wicket, no longer rising to the bait when their appearance together in the Woolpack set the gossips' tongues wagging.

Then, on the eve of the annual cricket match between Beckindale and neighbouring Robbelsfield, while the village team practised in the nets under the eagle eye of club president Sam Pearson, Joe wandered over to Kathy and they kissed for the first time since Kathy had left. Old Sam Pearson watched, worried, deeply disturbed. Did they know no shame? 'There are duties,' he explained later to Annie. 'They are both married. There's a right way and a wrong way. Joe doesn't think about talk in t'village, does he?'

Sam represented the old morality, not the brimstone variety which fired Jim Gimbel, but the one he'd grown up in, which put the community first. 'No-one can live life proper,' he told his grandson, 'without thinking of others.' But Joe took a different view. 'The older I get,' he told Kathy, 'The clearer I see that the only way is to go your own way.' Perhaps he'd been more influenced by his older brother than he cared to admit.

Emotions at Holly Farm began again to boil up in the heat of Joe and Kathy's rekindled passion. Martin was talking about leaving home, possibly joining the army. And once again Kathy was beginning to recoil at the gossip and considered returning to Hotten.

'You can't hide,' she told Joe, 'Not even at Hawthorn. You step out of line in a place like Beckindale, and folks won't let you forget in a hurry.'

Joe meanwhile was beginning to see that being free entailed a measure of courage.

'You know our trouble, don't you?' he said one day to Kathy. 'We're cowards . . . The fact is we can't get married, not yet, but we do want to live together. Now there's nothing to stop us doing that is there?'

That was how it happened. That was how new ground was broken in Beckindale, as easily as clods of clay by the frost.

'Do you mean at Hawthorn?' Kathy asked, as if skirting the main issue.

'No,' said Joe. 'I've got to sell that. But I could buy a cheaper place in t'village.'

'But if we were to live together like man and wife, could you face your family and the village?'

Here then was the crunch. But it was Kathy presenting it to Joe, not the other way round, Kathy whose family's reaction would be far more explosive than Joe's, Kathy who had already been forced out of Beckindale by the reaction of family and village to the affair. Clearly Kathy had already made her mind up to make the bigger leap, and simply wanted Joe to give her the encouragement she needed.

'I could,' he said, looking into her eyes. 'Could you?'

'I . . . Aye, I could,' there was barely a hint of a falter, before Kathy moved positively forward to – 'When?'

'As soon as we've found a place together.'

A few days later, again under the disapproving eyes of Sam Pearson, Joe took Kathy to Percy Edgar's place on Demdyke Row, in the heart of the village.

Percy had lived in Demdyke for many years, and inside the cottage, all that this aged Beckindaler embodied was all that Kathy could see. Instantly she recoiled –

'Everywhere you look there's an atmosphere, people who have lived here, stains on the wallpaper, smells in the cupboard . . .'

Kathy saw in the overlay of wallpaper and paint, patterns of what-had-been, all the repressive morality that she had come to hate. Joe misunderstood. She wouldn't recognise the place once he'd given it a lick of paint, he told her. But you don't strip away the spirit of a place as easily.

Standing there in Percy's dusty deserted cottage Kathy felt keenly what had been oppressing her about the cobwebby conventions of Beckindale. Freed of clutter, like the rooms she had been walking through, her mind saw clearly that what had once seemed supportive about the close village community from isolated Holly Farm was all too easily transformed into a suffocating claustrophobia.

'Here I get the feeling all the time like someone's looking over my shoulder . . .you've got houses on both sides pressing against you. You take Hawthorn, you get the impression there that people's lives were different, more free somehow . . . No thanks, Joe, it's not for me.'

Joe bought Demdyke anyway and Kathy shared it with him, partly because by that time she was an outcast in her own home. Another visit to Holly

Farm, in which Joe explained to Jim Gimbel what he intended to do with his daughter, excited the man to such anger that the complete disintegration of his family was just a matter of time. Martin would join the army, Freda and Davey would flee Gimbel's awesome wrath and settle with Freda's sister in Leeds.

Others reacted at their own level on a scale for which Jim Gimbel set the extreme. As Kathy feared, their neighbours at Demdyke, two gossiping spinster sisters, Prissy and Effie Carter, soon became more of a distraction than an amusement, and finally a source of indignation as their net curtains fluttered back and forth whenever Kathy came in. Gossip was rife. Sam Pearson was hurt to the quick – 'You read in the papers about the unrest and the lowering of standards and you never think that it belongs to you until it lands on your own doorstep. Aye, we've got it now at Emmerdale! . . . Joe and I, we live in different worlds.'

Only when Annie insisted he concede something to his favourite grandson did Sam admit, 'There's times old 'uns like me can't make out where the world's goin'. It's sometimes hard to know whether we're right or they're right . . . I mean the young 'uns.'

As for Annie, she had felt the inevitability of what was happening for a long time, as strongly as she felt protective towards her son. She had tried to help at

Joe and Kathy outside Percy Edgar's cottage at Demdyke, where Kathy sensed in the stains on the wallpaper and the smells in the cupboards a suffocating atmosphere of what-had-been.

the beginning – 'Joe,' she had called to him one day in the kitchen at Emmerdale, when she knew what was brewing in his mind, 'If there's anything you want to talk over . . .'

'Ma,' her son broke in, 'I'm just thinking of buying a cottage that's all.'

'Joe!' Annie stopped him in his tracks – she was never one to be hoodwinked – 'I'm talking about Kathy.'

'Yes, I know,' Joe admitted quietly, 'if anything happens I'll let you know.'

'Might be better if I knew before it happened. I'm on your side y'know.'

It might indeed have been better because soon Joe was way out of his depth. Fraught with feelings of guilt over the break-up of the Gimbel family, he and Kathy veered between argument and reconciliation, not knowing from one day to the next which way life would take them.

Then, late one day, ironically soon after they had been freed by divorce to marry and settle everyone's concern, a pained lowing was heard over Holly Farm – cows in milk aching for release.

No farmer ever forgot to milk his cows.

It was all over. Jim Gimbel had shot himself.

The Value of Life

Jim Gimbel had been convinced that there was an underlying fault in the moral bedrock of Beckindale due to a declining faith in God. But really to understand the people of the Dales, we must start at the root of their culture, even before Christianity came. We must start with the land and enter the magical relationship which the Dalesman has enjoyed with it since the beginning.

Beckindale, nestling in the lush green Dales.

The county of Yorkshire is by far the largest and most varied in England, but can be usefully thought of as being composed of four upland tracts separated by lowland areas.

In the northwest the lush green Yorkshire Dales rise steadily westwards along long broad ridges to windswept, rain-lashed moorland fells and North Pennine peaks over 2,000 feet high, beyond which lie Cumbria's Lake District and North Lancashire.

To the east, the Dales are separated by the Vale of York from the North York Moors which look southwards across the Vale of Pickering to the Wolds.

South of the Dales, across the Aire Gap, a confluence of road, railway, canal and river, lies the industrial powerhouse of the county (Leeds, Bradford,

Right: Kilnsey village in the shadow of the fell, where the annual fell race was held.

Kilnsey Crag, the indigenous limestone rock washed clean by passing glaciers and waterflows.

Sheffield and so on).

The limestone bedrock of the Dales erupted from the sea some 350 million years ago and was formed from the broken shells of millions of sea animals. But the broad floors and steep sides of the Dales were not opened up until the Ice Age, between one and two million years ago, when the alternate melting and freezing action and flow of gigantic ice forms (up to 1 km thick) moulded them to the spectacular shape we know today.

Sometimes the process can be seen quite clearly, for example at Kilnsey, where the indigenous limestone rock, washed clean by passing glaciers and water-flows, remains splendidly proud of any cover.

Kilnsey lies at the confluence of two rivers, the Wharfe and the Skirfare, which runs through Litton-dale, near the head of Wharfedale, where the story of Emmerdale unfolds. It was at Kilnsey that Joe Sugden, with Kathy's encouragement, entered the gruel-ling annual fell race in 1976, and Matt Skilbeck customarily showed Emmerdale's prize ewes at the annual show. From here, too, Emmerdale got its name. For, as the locals will tell you, the ancient name of Littondale was Ammerdale.

In places high on the limestone plateaux above the southern Dales the action of waterflows over centu-ries cut shakeholes and potholes into the bedrock. Here, at Baker's Pot, in the same year as Joe's fell

The fell race in 1976. Joe considers the reality of what he has taken on.

race, two Swedes, Olaf and Aster Gunnerson, very nearly came to grief in a 15-mile section of underground tunnels scoured out of the limestone.

As these limestone uplands dip gently to the north and east, the rock is overlaid by Yoredale beds, strata of limestone, sandstone and shale, capped by Millstone Grit. Centuries ago, the lead ore, building stone and thin seams of coal in the Yoredale beds attracted miners to the area, a legacy of which was ruefully inherited by the Sugdens in 1993, when Emmerdale Farm was virtually swallowed up by a disused mine.

Baker's Pot - 15 miles of underground tunnels, where Olaf and Aster Gunnerson came to grief in 1976.

Most of the farms, like Emmerdale built from stone quarried beneath the scree debris of the Yoredale beds, first appeared between 1670 and 1750, some to be rebuilt in the late 18th and early 19th centuries. But in many cases the stone-build was actually a case of renewal. For example, the buildings of Beckindale forming an enclosure around the village green, would have been replacements in different materials of buildings around a 6th or 7th century livestock corral.

There is archaeological evidence of Bronze Age settlers in the Dales since 3,000 BC and of Celtic settlers between 300 and 100 BC. The influence on the later Christian culture of Celtic times was enormous, the pagan fire festivals of the 3-year Celtic cycle – Samhain (November 1st), Lugnasadh (August 1st), Beltane (May 1st) and Imbolc (February 1st) – being re-named All Saints Day, Lammas (St Peter's Day), the feast day of St Michael the Archangel, and Candlemas respectively.

The first real momentum in farming came between

The broad floors and steep sides of the Yorkshire Dales (above and right) were etched out by glacial flows between one and two million years ago.

The farm buildings and homesteads built out of rock native to the place create a unique environmental unity, a unity which encompasses the character of the Dalesman too.

41

the 6th and 11th centuries AD when invading Angles (from North Germany) and Vikings (from Denmark, Norway and Sweden) established traditions of stock-holding, plant cultivation and the great tradition of pastoral farming we have today.

It was the pagan Vikings who gave us the word 'Dale' (it means 'valley') and bequeathed us other aspects of their language in many place names and in names of topographic features such as scar and crag.

The Vikings were the first really to establish the pastoral use of the rich and well-drained limestone soils of the Dales, grazing the valley pastures in Spring and Autumn and removing in the summer months to upland pasture like Pencross Fell, where the Sugden family has grazed its sheep and cattle since the 19th century.

Between the 12th and the 16th centuries the Norse traditions were developed by the landowning Christian monasteries until their dissolution between 1537 and 1540.

The monks were specialists in estate managment, operating the monastic 'mother farm' by means of a series of granges worked by locals. They also laid many of the roads and routes still followed, and began to build the drystone walls which contain the patchwork field design we know today.

The continuity of life in the Dales is extraordinary and the building of farm buildings and homesteads out of stone quarried from rock native to the place creates a unique environmental unity, which encompasses too the character of the Dalesman himself.

Farming here has always been tough. It bred a community of people as hardy as the heather which clings to the steep sides of the moor, but with a stoicism, patience and inner calm. Where visitors to the area might see nowt but stubbornness (the unyielding face of a landscape which has not really changed since the giant Ice Age glacial flows first formed it), closer acquaintance reveals characters which, like the impressionable limestone beneath the soil the Dalesmen farm, prove to be susceptible, albeit devilish deep down.

Left: The ruins of Bolton and Fountains abbeys, now as much a part of the landscape as any of the rock forms thrown up by Nature, are a reminder of the power of the Christian Church in the Dales in the Middle Ages. But it was not always so.

At the Seed Cut, an annual fertility rite practised since time immemorial, last year's Seed King gives ears of barley to the lads of the village. The one who draws the ear with most seeds leads the chase from the last field to be harvested to the village, where the winner chooses a Queen from among Beckindale's girls. The Beckstone Thrash was another age-old annual ceremony. Elders processed around the village boundary, thrashing their staffs on the ground to ward off evil spirits.

In the days when men were literally shaped by the land and the land was shaped by them from morning till dusk, nature and man were part of one another in a way that influenced life not only in the fields.

The power of some of our greatest novels celebrate this special communion of rural people with their environment. Thomas Hardy, albeit a southerner, even conjured up his own Beckindale to describe it – 'one of those sequestered spots where, from time to time, dramas of a grandeur and unity truly Sopho-clean are enacted in the real, by virtue of the concentrated passions and closely-knit interdependence of the lives therein.' He was describing the hamlet of Little Hintock (Hermitage in Dorset) in a novel called *The Woodlanders*, but transplanted a few hundred miles to the north it may as well have been Beckindale.

The spirit of rural England had its roots in a time before the Christians had reinterpreted and replaced pagan culture, and relics of pagan culture were still

High up on the moors, standing stones bear witness to a civilisation thousands of years old. Away in the distance modern totems (radomes) bring the picture up to date.

visible in the 1970s. For example, Beckindale's annual celebration of the Seeding Cut and the Beckstone Trash (captioned on page 43) can be traced back long before Christianity to Celtic and even earlier pagan rites.

Many of the pagan customs which survive today in rural England reflect the simple truth that the farming calendar is determined by the seasons, themselves determined by the movement of the earth round the sun. Children dancing around the maypole on May Day is the most obvious re-enactment of this. Other May Day dances, such as the Furry Dance in Helston or the Hobby Horse in Padstow, Cornwall, are a celebration of the same thing. Every mythology contains instances of it, the earliest known choreographic example being set in a mosaic on the floor in front of the palace at Cnosus in Crete. It was created by Daedalus for Ariadne, the daughter of King Minos, early in the second millennium BC.

In the case of Beckindale's Seeding Cut, so named because it was conducted at harvest time on the land of the farmer last in with the barley, the message was clear. In the end of one annual cycle lay the seeds of the next, symbolised ritualistically in last year's Seed-

Suddenly changing climatic conditions charge the landscape with its special beauty.

ing King passing ears of corn to the lads of the village and the coming together of the new year's Seeding King and Queen.

When young Joe Sugden raced off across Emmerdale's land in the summer of '73 and chose his Queen from among the pretty girls of Beckindale by kissing her, he was re-enacting a fertility rite which had been celebrated in the Dales for thousands of years and which re-affirmed that the impetus of rural culture lay in the birth-life-and-death cycle to which all life must bow. Rural peoples were closest to the cycle, they worked it with their hands. They were inseparable from their environment. Indeed, in some extraordinary way, they were their environment.

It was from this well of rural experience, deeper than either Jack's or Edward Ruskin's or Jim Gimbel's, that Annie drew. It did not falsify Christianity. Annie was the vicar's churchwarden. But it was the source of her intuitive wisdom.

Cultures which embrace people and environment are not of course only rurally based. Those formed during the Industrial Revolution around the shipyards of the Tyne, for example, or in the East End of London, were equally idiosyncratic. The former has been celebrated by Britain's biggest selling author, Catherine Cookson, the latter on television. But the spirit of rural culture cuts deeper because it describes the birth-life-death cycle, which is the essence of life. When Jack returned to Beckindale in 1980, he would describe it as 'the flow of life', which his literary cavortings abroad had missed.

Very often, where regional cultures were truest, there was great poverty which bound folk together. This was the case in the country as well as in the town. And yet the view persisted that the culture of the country was preferable to the culture of the city. City capitalism lived off its workers. Life in the country was natural. It fed its people. It was where man's roots lay. It was a place to be real and true. As Thomas Hardy put it in Far From the Madding Crowd, 'God was palpably present in the country, and the devil had gone with the world to town.'

Not everyone could see it. When Henry Wilks bumped into Janet Thompson, the woman he once nearly married some 30 years before, she couldn't believe that he, the successful industrialist, had found real enjoyment mingling with the likes of

After Marian left and Inglebrook burned down in 1973, Henry Wilks invested in the Woolpack and moved in with Amos. Together they made it the real focal point of the village.

Amos, old Walter and Seth in the Woolpack.

'Is this all an act?' she demanded of him, 'or do you really mean it? This "back-to-the-grass-root" thing. That's the correct term isn't it? Must be times when you miss it all. The business lunches in those old hotels, your sort of people. Oh, I'm not decrying your new friends, but is it enough?'

Henry's response was to explain to Janet that settling had been 'an attitude of mind,' and Janet replied as if he meant it was an artificial one, 'It's not easy to keep up an attitude for the rest of your life.'

In fact, after an unpromising start, Henry settled easily in Beckindale. He became a shareholder in three of its businesses, first Emmerdale Farm Ltd, then the Woolpack (he actually moved in with Amos after Inglebrook burned down) and for a time the village shop, when Alison Gibbons was in charge. But it wasn't Henry's money which helped him settle, rather his predisposition to the rural life. Henry was no farmer and never would be, but he was a countryman from the start, and being an obsessive bird watcher as well as a successful industrialist, he had a sense of nature and man's place in it.

His coming to Beckindale was a sign that he wanted to trade in something of the predatory nature of the peregrine falcon he so admired for its freedom on the air waves above Blea Head. He had made his pile in Bradford but unlike Janet he was not content. Janet was wrong in thinking that Henry's quest had called for sacrifice. Henry may himself have been surprised that he should have been made so welcome by Annie not just into the business but into the bosom of her family. But, as he soon learned, Annie wouldn't have had him as a shareholder on any other terms.

The place in Beckindale where 'the flow of life' could best be seen day-to-day was in the Woolpack. In 1977, the same year in which Joe sold Hawthorn Cottage and moved with Kathy into Demdyke Row, Henry, by then well ensconced with Amos behind the bar, suggested that since Amos had taken on the job of correspondent for the Hotten Courier, they hire an

The Woolpack today, the place in the village where the 'flow of life' can best be seen day-to-day.

Dolly Acaster shows Amos around Ephraim Monk's brewery.

assistant to help out.

Amos had given up any ideas of teaming up with a woman in marriage for the good of the business or for any other reason. It is not difficult to see why. Two minutes in the Woolpack itself described the kind of man Amos was better than an hour in his company (which could be quite confusing). The pub was cleanly and efficiently run, but there were no creature comforts. The decor was plain, somewhat worn and rather spare. In short, it was a man's pub without a hint of femininity, other than Amos's own rather fussy nature. In point of fact femininity rather disturbed Amos and when Henry presented him with an attractive personable blonde by name of Dolly Acaster as the new assistant, Amos was appalled.

He became even more concerned when Dolly went down well with the locals not only in the pub but in the village, where her experience as a set designer was soon employed in preparations for a village concert. Hurtfully, Amos vented his irritation in finicky criticism of Dolly, and soon she left to take up an offer to run a pub of her own near Leeds.

Such were the demands to keep up with the times even in Amos's well-ordered world, however, that a call for Real Ale by the Woolpack regulars found Amos exploring the mysteries of Ephraim Monk's brewery. And who should be assigned to take him on a guided tour, but the same Dolly Acaster.

Dolly, who had by this time left the Leeds pub to work at Monk's, was offered her old job back by Henry. For a while she even lived in the Woolpack, the sight of her lingerie on the clothesline filling Amos with confusingly contradictory impulses, always decently suppressed.

Amos was essentially a good man. But to anyone who didn't know him, the figure he cut of a fussily correct but well-drilled NCO – he was proud to have served as an artillery man – looked plain ridiculous.

But if Amos's act had ever been nurtured, it had long since become completely natural. And while it astonished visitors like Janet Thompson, it was highly regarded by the Woolpack's new brewery (which later referred to it as 'the Amos factor') and amused and endeared him to his regulars. The Woolpack was far and away the preferred watering hole, leaving the Malt Shovel at the other end of Beckindale to a mainly out-of-village clientele.

With Henry, Amos developed an extraordinary relationship, probably closer than with anyone else in the village. A few years earlier, the no-nonsense industrialist would scarcely have warmed to Amos's pernickety ways. And it was a mark of Henry's even temper (and perhaps his own loneliness after his daughter Marian had been driven abroad by Jack's lack of commitment) that he not only tolerated Amos's behaviour but developed a repartee with him which provoked the Swede Olaf Gunnerson to remark that he and Amos shared a relationship 'like in a marriage'.

There was more than a grain of truth in it. In time, their uneven banter would humanise both pub and publican, the change in Amos being given its measure by Annie herself. In 1995, four years after Henry's death, she agreed to marry him, even proposed it herself, twenty years after her put-down refusal.

Whether caroling outdoors (above, outside the original Woolpack before structural damage occasioned its move in 1977), or performing indoors in the village hall, as in Gilbert and Sullivan's The Pirates of Penzance *(1984, shown below), the spirit of fellow-feeling in Beckindale is clear.*

Back in 1977, with Henry and Dolly on board, the Woolpack began to add real momentum to the flow of life in Beckindale.

As Joe Sugden and Kathy Davis discovered, the close weave of the Beckindale community was a breeding ground for gossip and rumour capable of spreading like a virus. But in the very different context of events like the village shows, concerts, harvest festivals, pantomimes and Jubilee street parties, the self-same weave lay open to a spirit of fellow-feeling which was about to be put to the test in the annual cricket match with neighbouring Robbelsfield.

Each year Beckindale and Robbelsfield waged war

for the Butterworth Ball. It was a prize no less important than the Ashes to the nation. For weeks beforehand the match commanded the attention of great' strategists on and off the field, which, in Beckindale's case, meant club chairman Sam Pearson.

Cricket, of course, occupies a special place in the life of many a village, but never more so than in the villages of Yorkshire, where it is something of a religion.

On this occasion, in the summer of 1977, Robbelsfield had caught Beckindale on the hop, requesting an evening game without Sam even considering that they might have a hidden agenda. Perhaps he had been too taken up with Joe and Kathy. More likely he was over-confident, having found himself a secret weapon – a new fast bowler – by name of Granger.

As the day drew near, thinking he was leaving nothing to chance, Sam had his men down on all fours inspecting the pitch. Granger had swing as well as speed. If Robbelsfield were to feel him at his best, the pitch must be perfect for Granger's strike. All seemed set when Sam received a phone call from Amos telling him that a man had been asking questions in the Woolpack about Beckindale's team. Then it emerged that the same man had been seen at the ground while Sam's men had been looking over the wicket. Worse still, the man's name was Phil Kitson. Henry had been at Emmerdale when the call came through. Sam let Kitson's name drop as he made for the door, grabbing his coat as he went. Joe looked at Annie and Matt, and then at Henry, bemused. Who was Phil Kitson? 'The only Phil Kitson I've ever heard of,' Henry sighed, 'used to play for minor counties.'

Later, Sam Pearson confirmed it was he: 'Robbelsfield have got Phil Kitson from Berkshire,' and Kitson was not only an ex-pro bowler he was a batsman too, an all-rounder. It was the final straw. As Henry said, 'You can't expect village cricket to stand up to his kind of bowling.'

To look at Sam, you would have thought that his whole world had caved in, and Kitson's annihilation of Beckindale on the day – 28 all out – looked like the beginning of their wholesale humiliation.

At the end of Beckindale's innings, Sam, umpiring for the village, moved towards the wicket as his opposite number called: 'We'll have a break now,

shall we? Half an hour and I reckon we'll be going back home.'

Sam snatched up the bales angrily from the stumps and buried his chin in his chest, deep in thought. 'We're not beat yet,' he muttered to Matt as he came over.

'Not yet, but we will be, Grandad,' was Matt's careless reply.

Furious at Matt's defeatism, Sam exploded – 'You've got no faith have you?' – and stomped off back to the Pavilion.

It was bad enough for Sam that Robbelsfield had taken the trophy last year too. Now Joe learned that the reason they'd asked for an evening match was to enable Kitson to play. The man had recently taken a shop in Robbelsfield village, and he would not have been able to play during working hours. Beckindale had lost this time both on and off the pitch. And it was all down to Sam.

So sure and short seemed the path to defeat that while Joe had a drink at the Woolpack with Kitson during the break, Amos, perhaps unable to digest Beckindale's humiliation without first breaking it down into a more easily manageable form, was gushing in his praise of the ex-pro and did all but attach his colours to Kitson's team. Henry couldn't believe what he was hearing. But Amos found all the justification he felt he needed in 'facing the facts', as he put it. Amos was not a sporting man. Sam was, however, and had he been there, he might have told Amos that much depended on which facts you chose to line up before you.

'We need fifteen minutes,' the Robbelsfield umpire declared as he strode back on to the pitch for his side's innings. 'Matter of fact we didn't even bother to bring Butterworth Ball with us,' he threw at Sam. 'We knew, y'see?'

Granger's first ball thundered down the wicket and then an extraordinary thing happened. Not, as expected by Robbelsfield, the wet smack of willow against leather as the ball found the centre of the bat of Berkshire's best. Not, as longed for by the daydreamers in the field, the dull thud of ball against pad followed by a sharp 'Owzat!' It was a sound, certainly, and the impact it had on the game was terminal. But it wasn't anything to do with cricket.

What everyone heard was the slow painful wail of a siren calling Beckindale's firemen from the field, the sound building in a crescendo with the incredulity of the Robbelsfield team. It brought the game to a resounding halt.

'The Lord moves in mysterious ways,' Sam chuckled to himself, 'his mysteries to perform.'

Back at the Woolpack everyone had to agree that the match had been formally abandoned. The departing players would not be back in time to resume the game before bad light stopped play.

'So we toss then!' Sam concluded triumphantly as he saw the odds narrow to 50/50.

'I don't know . . .' whined Robbelsfield's umpire, scanning the bar for support.

'Well that's the rules,' said Sam, waving the rule book in front of his nose. 'Paragraph 7: Abandoned match should be decided by toss of coin. You've got no choice.'

Granger came up tails.

'We've done it!' cried Sam unabashed. 'I'm buying everyone a drink!'

The lengths the old stallwarts of Beckindale would go in those days to maintain and protect the honour of the village knew no bounds. The Butterworth Ball itself was returned to pride of place behind the bar and never a day went by when Sam's eyes would not fall upon it as he supped his pint.

Until one day, they didn't. Sam's eyes passed over the bar, but the ball was not there. At first he couldn't believe it.

'Where's t'Butterworth Ball?' he asked in a low expressionless voice. Amos and Henry followed his eyes to the cabinet and a shocked silence enveloped the three of them and spoke more profoundly than any words of the horror in their souls.

When fury replaced shock, poor Dolly, responsible for cleaning the bar, was first in the frame. She gave her evidence coolly and clearly. The ball had been there yesterday but she hadn't touched it. She knew better than to touch it, she only ever flicked it clean. Heaven forbid she should soil the sacred relic with her hands.

Then fury was tempered by reason, and Amos and Henry put the fact of the missing ball together with the disappearance they'd noticed earlier of a large amount of whisky from one of the dispensers. Earlier that day, when the two proprietors of the Woolpack came down to open up the bar, Amos, ever observant for the smallest detail out of line, had checked with

Umpire and Club President Sam Pearson knew that in village cricket the game is not always won or lost on the pitch.

Henry as to whom he'd served with whisky during the latter part of the evening. Neither had been able to account for the discrepancy and they'd concluded that someone must have remained in the bar after they had locked up and gone to bed. Perhaps the culprit had hidden in the toilet . . . What was clear was that nothing other than the ball and the whisky had gone missing.

The finger pointed at Robbelsfield.

'It's them!' Sam exclaimed, bringing the investiga-

Cricket occupies a special place in the life of many a Dales village, but the occasion in 1977 of the annual match between Beckindale and neighbouring Robbelsfield, pictured here, is not likely ever to be forgotten.

tion to a conclusion, 'It's the Robbelsfield lot!' – the motive, pique at the decision over the game and a desire to make Beckindale look foolish.

It was then that Dolly had her say. If Sam was right, the one thing they must not do was to report the ball missing. A sure way to undermine Robbelsfield's strategy was to replace the ball with another.

Sam could't believe his ears. That Dolly – a woman! – could have come up with such a solution. The original ball must be found of course, but Dolly's idea would leave the honour of Beckindale unsullied.

For months, Sam had been complaining about a blossoming relationship between Matt and Dolly, Matt who had been married to his darling Peggy, God rest her soul. How could he marry again? Now, all of a sudden, Dolly could do no wrong. As far as Sam was concerned anyone who had such a keen eye for the good of the village was absolutely irreproachable.

Amos focused everyone's minds back on the business to hand. Perplexed that there might be an attempt to examine the ball and face them with their deceit, he insisted they rig up an alarm which would ring if the ball was lifted from its perch. Unfortunately, when they wired up the system, the alarm only rang when the ball was in place, and they had to disarm it.

With the kind of inevitability which attends only the best comic routines when real life mimics art, Fred Teaker, licensee of the Miller's Arms in Robbelsfield, was among the first of Amos's customers that evening.

Was Teaker surprised to see that there was a cricket ball in the Butterworth cabinet? Would he ask to inspect it? What in his behaviour would point to

Robbelsfield's guilt in the affair?

Teaker's neat footwork was astonishing. Announcing that the Miller's Arms was shortly to be celebrating its bicentennial, Teaker informed Amos that he planned to make the Butterworth Ball a focal point of their celebrations. Amos realised he couldn't refuse Teaker. The ball was common property.

Playing for time (and praying that Sam would not come into the pub), he said that only the president of the cricket committee could possibly grant permission.

But then, becoming over-confident, Amos boasted to Teaker of how seriously he took his responsibility as keeper of the ball. He even shared with his adversary a description of the alarm system he had rigged up as security, only realising what he had let himself in for when Teaker made his second wholly reasonable request – that Amos show him how the system worked.

It was rare for Amos actually to taste the bitter fruits of his woeful relationship with life. His undisguised absurdity so endeared him to people that time and again they rescued him from himself. But now Amos had no option but to walk-the-plank and drown in a sea of humiliation. He must comply with Teaker's request. There was no way out. Yet Amos knew that the alarm wouldn't work, and that when it didn't, Teaker would absolutely insist on inspecting the ball.

Amos took the few paces towards the replacement ball and stretched up to where it sat in a niche behind the bar, his hand hovering for a moment above it, hesitating like a man savouring the last moment of life before the big drop. Then his fingers felt the rough surface of the well-used ball and he lifted it from its perch.

How does the drowning man feel? Is death immediate and then . . . nothing? Or are there flashing lights . . .and ringing ships' bells? For a moment Amos was unsure whether the brisk brrr-inging in his ear was sentence or reprieve.

Later, after Teaker had retreated, Henry settled Amos's nerves by explaining that he had watched his every movement from the back room and timed his manual activation of the alarm system to coincide with Amos's lifting it from its perch.

The battle was won but the war far from over. If luck comes twice to those who make their own, Amos, Henry and Sam must have been doing something right. Later, a woman turned up at the pub and offered them information that would lead them to the ball . . . for a price.

Under questioning it emerged that the woman's name was Lil and that she was the girlfriend of Teaker's brother – the felon who had stolen the ball – and with whom Lil had a score to settle.

Amos was outraged. Failing to weigh in the balance the deceit rife on both sides in the affair, he refused to pay over the money. Henry couldn't believe it and stepped in to offer Lil £10. She told him that the Butterworth Ball had been lobbed into the vicarage garden on the night of the raid.

Under cover of dark, by the lights of a car, Henry, Amos and Sam undertook their search . . .and found nothing.

The village scout troop had cleared the garden the day after the theft, and Billy Luttercombe, who had found the ball, had been made a present of it by the vicar. Worse, as Annie informed them, the Luttercombes were away for the Christmas break which would include the period of the bicentenary celebrations at the Miller's Arms.

Sam was all for breaking into the Luttercombes' house, but Annie suggested that a chat with Bessie Aspinal, Billy's aunt, might be preferable. Eventually only a 600-mile round trip to Torquay and back by Henry would suffice, and all they had to show for it was the news that Billy had lost the ball in the village allotments before leaving for holiday.

Meanwhile events at home had ground mercilessly on. Teaker had turned to vengeance and called in PC Dawes. In front of his customers, Amos was faced with the indignity of an investigation as to why the burglary had not been reported, and had to admit before Teaker and the regulars of the Woolpack his own deceit.

Then, at the moment of Robbelsfield's victory and Amos's total humiliation, Annie bustled in from the village jumble sale and produced . . .the ball. Willie Ockroyd had found it in his cold frame and tossed it in a bag of jumble for the sale.

The story of the Butterworth Ball has something of almost mythical status in the annals of Beckindale's history. Yet it has none of the landmark significance attached to the fall of the Squirearchy or the move from subsistence farming to agribusiness or the move in general away from farming to tourism, which are stories of largescale economic and social significance to the history of the village and will colour the coming years.

What it has is a sort of organic completeness. It seems to occur in a very English rural cultural cocoon. Of course it helps that it centres on cricket. As recently as the 1920s it was still possible to write that cricket was the one and only outdoor game which had remained purely English. Some might argue that the game of English cricket is even now played only in England, even only at village level, and that any game played elsewhere by the same name is something rather different.

The tradition of village cricket grew in an era when England was largely a patchwork of villages whose inhabitants lived and died there, and rarely travelled far. Loyalty and club identity are two of the defining marks of cricket at village level, they are its lifeblood and, to Sam, they were also the lifeblood of a community where balance is maintained not by the fire and brimstone of Jim Gimbel's God, nor by the arm of secular law – we know at once that PC Dawes will not be the deciding factor – but by a force built into the very fabric of Beckindale.

What was on offer across the bar of the Woolpack and in the close-weave of the Beckindale community in those days had something to do with what Annie understood by the value of life.

What threatened her idea of the value of life in Beckindale was not a loss of faith in Jim Gimbel's God; that was an effect, for good or bad. What redefined the Dalesman's idea of the value of life was a process begun by the Industrial Revolution in the 19th century associated with his alienation from the land, the relationship which had defined his unspoken, intuitive sense of the spirit in things.

It is worth quantifying the process. In 1801, around four-fifths of the population of Britain lived in villages or very small towns; by 1851, half the nation had moved to cities or large towns; by 1901, three-quarters. The nearly one million agricultural labourers in 1851 had been cut by a third fifty years later.

In the 20th century a scientific revolution in farming, aimed at increased efficiency and profit, completed the transition. As the '70s gave over to the '80s, it would finally catch up with Beckindale and the old perception of the value of life began to change.

In 1974, newly shored up with Henry's finance, Emmerdale Farm Ltd, under Joe's day-to-day management, had invited a production analyst to advise how best to proceed towards a high yield, low cost farming strategy.

Christine Sharp was the daughter of a gentleman farmer, who was also in the woollen industry. Her father was rich. Christine wanted for nothing materially. She was well-educated and altogether 'top drawer'.

But when she turned up at Emmerdale she found something she had only ever dreamed about. Farming for Christine's father was simply a way to deal with his tax problems. He didn't get his hands dirty in the soil. But at Emmerdale the daily round was as it had been for centuries – real farming, real contact with the cycle of life. Christine could smell it, see it, feel it in a way that she had only dreamed she might. And she wanted it, needed it, more than anything else. The route she chose to secure it for herself was Joe.

Henry wondered at the way Christine was making all the running for Joe. Something about it seemed not quite right. Maybe he had a better sense than most of the irony of a productivity adviser falling for the lure of the rural spirit, and the difference in Christine's and Joe's backgrounds and bank accounts bothered Annie too.

Problems began to emerge as soon as they became engaged, when a rich friend of Christine was bought a dazzlingly expensive engagement ring.

What was immediately clear was that Joe couldn't compete. Henry, desperate not to see Joe disappointed, fixed up a discount on a similar ring with a friend of his in the trade. But it was Annie, seeing through the thing to the core, who decided to make a lesson out of it, which both Joe and Christine would do well to learn. As Joe thrashed about in his sea of uncertainty, Annie threw him a lifebelt in the shape of a Victorian engagement ring, which far outshone the one worn by Christine's rich friend, not in glitz but in true value.

The ring had belonged to Jacob's mother, it was family, it belonged to the simple longstanding rural

With Emmerdale Farm bolstered up by Henry's finance, Joe had pressed ahead with plans to have his cow herd accredited as free from tuberculosis, a big investment in both time and money. In 1974, he applied to the Milk Marketing Board for a production analyst to advise him on the best strategy for his dairy business. They sent him Christine Sharp, pictured with Joe, above. Her analysis of the situation would not be confined to farming.

tradition called Sugden; in that sense it was priceless, it had a value which could not be bought.

This theme of value runs right through the story of Emmerdale, the difference between monetary and true value, as Annie defined it. In Christine and Joe's short marriage it turned out to be no more nor less than the difference between illusion and reality. Christine's desire for Emmerdale, her desire to be absorbed into the spirit of rural England by marrying Joe was unsustainable in the light of day because

she could not truly give herself to it.

When she found she needed to draw on artificialities and lies to keep her fantasy alive, Joe was left wondering what on earth had been going on. Then, by chance, he met Christine's father at Loudwick market, who explained all: 'She's a dreamer . . . She gets fantasies and follows them. At the moment the fantasy is to be a farmer's wife – to plant and sow and reap and mow . . . But it won't last long – nothing ever does with her.'

Joe didn't believe it. But their marriage lasted only as long as the honeymoon.

It took a 16-year-old girl from Middlesborough to express most succinctly this spirit of Emmerdale, which Christine wanted.

Rosemary Kendall was the waifish daughter of an old friend of Annie, who was severely ill with depression. As a result, in 1975, shortly after Joe's marriage to Christine Sharp had broken down, Rosemary was brought to live at Emmerdale.

Beatrix Potter once wrote that 'it sometimes happens that the town child is more alive to the fresh beauty of the country than a child who is country born.' Certainly, for Rosemary, the joy she experienced in the sights and sounds of Emmerdale seemed to be heightened by the fact that they were wholly new to her. The sounds of the farm, and the sights and smells of the countryside appealed to Rosemary as first-time experiences do before they are tarnished by habit and similitude.

There was innocence in her response, where for Christine there had been purpose. Rosemary's innocence would be shattered, but she would learn from the experience. At first, like Christine, she saw the spirit of Emmerdale imbued in Joe. She developed a teenage crush on him, though Joe remained blissfully unaware. At first, her vision of farm and countryside was of a completer harmony of all things with each other than she had ever known, which was why it hurt her so when she discovered what was real.

It was the day before her seventeenth birthday and she was having tea with Annie, Sam, Matt and Joe in the kitchen at Emmerdale Farm. Nothing could have been more to Rosemary's liking and she thrilled to the idea Joe had for giving her a birthday calf. It was an old family tradition – the first calf born after midnight on the eve of a birthday. As it happened, 'We had twin calves born one o'clock this morning.'

Going out to meet her calf she immediately gave it a name, Frosty, because he had a white mark on his forehead.

Something made Joe hesitate, 'We don't generally bother with names except for milkers, Rosemary,' he told her. But Rosemary insisted. How else would she be able to talk to the calf when she was looking after him? Joe and Annie eyed each other. Annie shared Joe's caution and explained to the girl that there was no need for her actually to do anything with the calf, the gift was a birthday token, that was all. Then Matt chimed in, rather less sensitively, saying that being given a birthday calf meant that Rosemary

Sunset over Wharfedale delivers the romantic picture visitors associate with the Dales.

would get whatever it fetches.

'Fetches?' asks Rosemary, her small voice a-quiver.

'When it's sold,' said Joe.

'Sold?'

'Aye. That's what we rear 'em for.'

The rest of the conversation was no more than a distant echo to Rosemary's ears. It had never occurred to her that farms raised calves for people to eat, that no bull calf was kept on a dairy farm, that they were conceived to keep the herd in milk and then sold at market for beef.

'What does she think happens on a farm?' Joe said when Rosemary flew from the room. 'That we keep animals until they die of old age?'

Even some youngsters who grow up on a farm find it difficult to come to terms with the killing. Many have written of their first experience of it, often with the annual pig-killing in mind. Flora Thompson, who grew up in the wheat growing hamlet of Juniper Hill in Oxfordshire, referred to it in her book, *Lark Rise to Candleford*, as a scene 'as savage as anything to be seen in the African jungle', and Alison Uttley, child of Castle Top Farm near Cromford in Derbyshire, described how, as a girl, she'd retire 'to the top of the house where she lay with her fingers in her ears' to silence the pig's squealing as its throat was cut.

From that moment, life demanded of Rosemary Kendall a response. No-one could respond for her. Rosemary must give of herself. As Annie said to Matt when he made to go after her, 'Nay, lad, let her alone. She's got to take it in, and she's best by herself when she does.'

Her response came the following day when another cow calved. Joe fetched Sam Pearson from the house and together they dashed into the calf-house, leaving Rosemary staring at the kitchen door. It was a difficult birth, messy, and when Joe looked up from his knees in the straw and saw Rosemary standing by the calf-house door, he said, 'Nay, Rosemary, this isn't for thee –'

But Rosemary insisted she stay to watch the gory business. Sam told her to go back to the kitchen, but she dug her heels in and reluctantly they did allow her to stay.

Rosemary watched as Sam and Joe went about their business with a dexterity and warmth which

Rosemary was despondent when her romantic view of life at Emmerdale was dashed. But she was prepared to learn and what she discovered was something far more mysterious and deep-set in Nature.

seemed to draw them in as partners with the animals in what was going on. Everyone, man and animal, was part of the mysterious unending round, the birth-life-death cycle, Annie's touchstone, which now seemed to Rosemary to be bigger and more inevitable than any ideas she might have about what was proper. There was only one way Rosemary could conceive of going, and that was to become a part of it too.

'He . . . he seems a bit weak,' her voice trembled across the shed to the men when it was all over.

'He's not a hundred per cent,' Sam agreed. 'Needs looking after.'

'Can I do it?

The men looked at one another and Sam began, 'Nay, lass . . .'

'I don't want him to be my calf, something special or anything like that,' she reassured them. Rosemary didn't want him like a person wants a pet.

Joe relented. If she wanted to help, Rosemary would have to keep track of his temperature. There was every likelihood the vet would be needed. And then Joe turned to the calf and said, 'Hear that, little 'un. You've got to make a bit of an effort now, haven't you – with a nurse like this.'

'A Damn Good Shake-up'

After the break-up of his marriage to Laura, George Verney had moved to France, and his residence, the Hall at Home Farm, had been used as a teacher training college. In 1978, after George died, his son, Gerald, faced with death duties of £600,000, put Home Farm and all the Estate up for sale.

Sam was aghast at the news. The Squierarchy was a hereditary institution. He couldn't believe that a Verney would fail to meet his responsibilities to Beckindale whatever the financial pressures on him.

Sam's world turned on considerations of tradition and continuity, but that wasn't the only reason why it wouldn't occur to him to question the old order. A Squire's right to pecuniary advantage over his tenant farmers was earned. Sam had no time for a Socialist ethic which held that a tenant's obligation to the Squire in some way lowered a tenant's standing or self-esteem. It was not his experience and it would not have made sense to him. The Squire's tenants couldn't have afforded to farm on their own account, and the influence of the Squire benefited the community in many other ways.

'When that big house up there is empty,' Sam said, 'it's like a hole in the wall of our local society. Warmth and friendship seem to seep away through it. When the Verneys were there, they gave parties and had folk there for discussion of local affairs, and the Hunt met there and the mummers used to perform there, and they always came to the Nativity Play, and could be relied on to open a fete or judge a competition . . .'

To Sam, the sale of the Verney Estate meant the end of an era in which tenant farmers in the area had been looked after by a generous Squire, and Beckindale had benefited from Verney's patronage at dances, concerts, flower shows and so on.

Sam believed that property which was legally owned by the Squire actually belonged, in a sense that cut deeper than common law, to Beckindale. He did not want to see it pass into private ownership, into the hands of someone who wouldn't care for the people of Beckindale. What would happen to tenant

farmers who ran their farms on a shoestring and fell behind with the rent?

Sam was right to worry, for henceforth Estate business would be run strictly according to principles of

George Verney, Squire of Beckindale, with Dr Clare Scott at the Harvest Festival in 1973.

profit and economy; any advantage sought by tenants on any other basis would be very hard won.

True to his upbringing, Sam tried to organise an official reception for Gerald Verney on his arrival at the Hall. But to his amazement he discovered that the vicar was not in favour, and Henry told him that he was too busy and couldn't imagine why Sam should think that a reception was necessary. Henry, a man of the 20th century, could see no reason to kow-tow to the Verneys, and it didn't occur to Sam that Henry had already taken over some of the patronage of Beckindale from the Squire.

Only Amos came across. With typical toadiness and the hidden agenda of an article for the Hotten Courier, Amos leapt at Sam's idea and delivered a pompous soliloquy over the phone, in which he offered Verney the 'compliments of the locality'. Unfortunately, Verney imagined that he had a lunatic on the line and slammed down the phone.

When Sam scoured the Courier for Amos's article he found in its place an advertisement for 'The Hall, Miffield Rise, nr. Beckindale . . . 10 bedrooms . . . built

1681 . . .' It was left to Annie to let the old man down gently: 'It's no good harking back to the old days when the folk at the Hall felt a responsibility for Beckindale . . . Fact of the matter is, this new lad has never seen us and doesn't know us.'

Gerald himself then drove the point home. As Verney's lawyers went over the leaseholds in detail it was discovered that the Sugdens were farming a piece of land which didn't belong to them, was not part of the freehold sale of land to Emmerdale Farm Ltd in 1973. Verney argued that either the Sugdens buy the field, known as Top Twenty, a 20-acre mea-

Home Farm, the Hall and gardens. Here, since the 17th Century, the Squire had exercised his patronage over Beckindale. Three hundred years later, it was up for sale and life would never be the same again.

dow farmed by Emmerdale since Jacob's time, or hand it back.

Faced with the challenge, Henry went to work and turned up a Right of Adverse Possession, by which the Sugdens would have a claim on the land in law, provided no rent had been paid for it. Those who played by the law could lose by the law, was Henry's approach. Perhaps he remembered his earlier tussle over the public right of way across the Sugdens' land.

But the Verneys didn't lose because it was discovered that a rent had been paid once a year at Christmas. The payment had been known as the Verney Bottle. Once a year Jacob had gone up to the Hall with a bottle of Scotch. It was not rent of course in any meaningful way, just an excuse for Verney and Jacob to share in a bit of good will at the end of the year, a fine example of the traditional, easy-going relationship between landlord and tenant. But it was enough to ensure that the Sugdens had to dip into their pockets now.

The rest of the Estate was bought by a conglomerate called NY Estates, a modern agribusiness based in Humberside, with farms all over the country and fields the size of prairies, battery hens and hormone beef. The Estate manager, one Trevor Thatcher (in 1979 the name already carried connotations not wholly benign), had recently returned from Kuwait where he had managed a herd of 2,000 milkers on high production yield, miles from any grass.

Thatcher began as he meant to go on, giving four weeks notice to 70-year-old Nellie Ratcliffe to quit her leasehold cottage, her home for the past 48

Sam with Nellie Ratcliffe, whose home for the past 48 years was the first target of NY Estates.

years. The dwelling was 'required in the interests of efficient agriculture for an agricultural worker.' Then 'Keep Out' notices were posted on Verney's Woods, where Beckindalers had been allowed to shoot for centuries.

These were instances (two of many) of a fundamental change that was taking place in Beckindale. By acting strictly according to the rule of law NY believed it was justified in its actions. The law was the final arbiter. This was not victimisation, it was the law. No-one could argue with it.

But the eviction of Nellie Ratcliffe was not made good by being law, and Beckindalers saw this, just as Annie had made Henry see it back in 1973. The ultimate effect of Thatcher's policy was to call the law into question, by showing that it could be exploited unfairly.

Invoking the law to sanction bullying – Nellie was given four weeks to quit after nearly half a century's residence – wouldn't bring people into line. It would cut people off from the law, and far from exhonerating NY from blame, it would eventually bring Thatcher's tenure of office to an end.

Thatcher lined up his head cowman, Steve Ashcroft, to move in to Nellie's cottage, and Steve sud-

There was uproar about the sale of the Hall, but Gerald Verney didn't have everything his own way. Among the artefacts for sale was a painting called Dillingham Crags. Francesca Zorelli, a friend of Marian Wilks and pictured left with Henry, Gerald and his wife Charlotte, came all the way from Rome but bid only for the painting. Convinced that it must be a masterpiece, Amos tried to 'up' the bidding, but Francesca bought it for £230. Later it was confirmed that the painting by Gerald's ancestor, one Oswald Verney, concealed an earlier work by Michelangelo Caravaggio called The Flight of the Martyrs from the Lions, valued at around £200,000. A strict moralist, Oswald had taken exception to the nakedness of Caravaggio's subject men and women and covered them up with his rendition of the Crags.

NY Estates, the new owners of Home Farm, had farms all over the country with fields the size of prairies.

denly found himself the subject of taunts and strange looks and muttered asides by people in the street. Then he and his family were refused service in the village shop, and Annie went to see the Council and then Steve. And before long NY's head cowman made it clear to Thatcher that he didn't want the move, and Nellie was left alone.

Annie had won an important point of principle, and the words she used to the Council made it clear what that principle was. She told the Council that 'Nellie Ratcliffe belongs here in Beckindale, as surely as the old owl that hoots in the church tower.' This wasn't mere sentiment. For hundreds of years this land-based community had drawn its legal rubric from what was fair and just according to natural law. Man's law might keep a lot of lawyers from going hungry, but it was a moveable feast. The law of Nature was absolute and deeply engrained in the moral fabric of Beckindale. It never changed. But man's law was relative to the developing needs of a society with a quite different concept of value, as

Annie had shown when she gave Christine Sharp her engagement ring. Even lawyers recognise the difference. Equity is a system of jurisprudence founded on natural justice and fair conduct, which supplements the common law and mitigates against its inflexibility.

Another good example of how the two concepts of law differ was shown when Seth Armstrong discovered that his rabbit snares had been removed from the grounds of the old Hall.

Seth, who followed that time-honoured profession of poacher, had kept his ear to the ground from the moment Trevor Thatcher came on the scene. He immediately sensed a threat.

The poacher, like his smuggler cousin on the coast a century earlier, made his living outside man's law. Yet, in Beckindale and a host of other rural villages up and down the country, right into the '70s you

NY Estates invested in up-to-date machinery and embraced the latest in scientific research and business theory. It was a marriage of convenience with profit its intended issue.

could be a poacher and still be deemed an honest man in all your dealings. Smuggling was even called 'fair-trading' in the 19th century and many turned a blind eye.

'Y'know,' Seth once explained to Trevor Thatcher, 'there've always been fellers that enjoy pitting their wits against all the protection put up for game birds. It's a tradition like . . . Old Mr Verney used to say it was better to take your losses and live a quiet life.'

The tradition originally owed much to poverty when the Industrial Revolution was dividing the masses into the 'haves' and 'have-nots'. But the vindication of the poacher harked back to an earlier time, before the enclosure of the land, before even the notion took hold that land could be bought. It harked back to a time when nature's law really did hold sway, and its values of good and evil could distinguish between a criminal and a man in need.

Time had moved on, Seth was not a poacher from

need, but the tradition survived and so did the need for a law based on natural justice and fair conduct, and Annie's resistance had spelled out the repressive nature of human law when allied to expediency and personal interest.

Inevitably, with the gradual alienation of man from nature, greater emphasis was laid on human law. In the same period, crime increased dramatically in Beckindale and by the '90s had become almost an accepted dynamic of society.

Of course, crime was not unknown in the area in times past. Much of it had been associated with intrusion upon farmers' livelihoods or with some warped practice with nature, very often to be dealt with swiftly by the people themselves.

Sheep rustling was (and is) an example of this, one recent case occurring in Beckindale in 1986. Matt had been out with his sheepdog, Nell, when they'd come upon a truck parked in an Emmerdale field.

In the trailer were two Swaledale sheep. Mowlam had another caught by the legs in the curve of his crook and was grabbing a third ewe, carrying it bodily to the trailer attached to his truck . . .all the while muttering drunkenly, 'Some men go for pretty girls, tum, tum, tum, tum, tum – for boys – but my true love is my own true love . . .and she makes a baahing noise.'

Matt, seeing what they were up to, shouted. Mowlam dived into the truck, but before he could get the engine started Matt had reached for the vehicle, which then lurched into life.

Matt, managing to open the door, grabbed Mowlam as the truck careered towards the trees out of control into a tree with a crunching and tinkling of metal and glass. Dazed from the impact Mowlam was pulled by Matt out of the van. But when they gathered themselves and Matt threw his first punch,

Matt Skilbeck grabbed Harry Mowlam by the throat and squeezed.

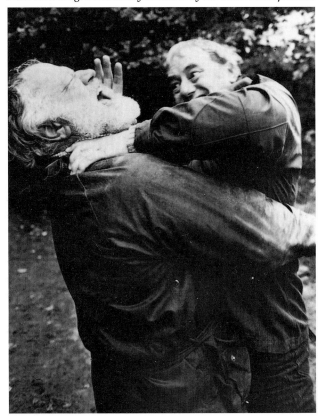

Mowlam ducked and laughed – 'I can take you Skilbeck. I can take you and the Sugdens any way I like. I could buy you out if I wanted to. I could buy out half of Beckindale.' It could have been anybody's result. Mowlam may have been drunk, but he was a big man and finally he took Matt in a huge bear hug which could have squeezed the life out of Matt had he not had his arms free to wind his fingers round Mowlam's throat. Suffering similar pressure on this more vulnerable point, Mowlam had to let him go, and it was then that Matt delivered a punch at Mowlam's head and the rustler staggered back and rolled down the bank to the stream. The fight was over and Matt moved at once towards Nell, who'd been kicked unconscious, and said, 'Alright girl, alright. Let's get thee home.'

The same year, there'd been a sighting of badgers in Verney's woods. They'd caught Amos's imagination to such an extent that he'd spent three evenings out of five observing them, leaving Henry to cope at the Woolpack.

'Didn't you tell me that badgers always share their work between them?' Henry had said to his partner rather testily.

'They do,' Amos had replied. 'They've got this innate urge to dig so they're always building. Oh, you should have seen them the other night, they were sniffing the air, having pretend fights, scratching their backs on a tree stump, it were magic!'

'I was wondering,' Henry said, pressing his point home, 'whether we couldn't take a leaf out of their book and share some of the work here . . .'

Amos was quite offended, 'I am pursuing a scientific interest of great potential value to the community. In time I might discover something about badgers that no-one ever knew before.'

Henry knew when he was beat and went to see what all the fuss was about. He was glad he had, until suddenly the peaceful scene of badgers going about their business was disturbed by the mechanical squark of a pheasant followed by the rustlings of badgers diving for cover. Then Henry heard the distinct footfall of man approaching, and he took cover as the headlamps of a car silhouetted a mass of confused images – three men carrying sacks and sticks, spades and torches, and excited terriers straining on leashes.

Badger-baiters at work. 'Keep digging,' the old man urged, 'I want the cubs too.'

Henry returned to the Woolpack and reported what he'd seen.

'I can't see what there is to get so worked up about,' said Seth, claiming the naturalist's high ground. 'A badger is no more than a 30-pound stoat.'

Henry described how he'd disturbed them when a fourth man had approached and blown a whistle, which had put the men into swift activity, nets in hand. By the time Henry had reached the site they were away. All that had been left was a pair of jagged toothed tongs on the ground.

Seth explained what badger-baiters did: 'They dig a trench, see, put the badger they catch down the end. Then they get about four terriers and put them in with him.'

'You mean to make them fight.'

'Aye, except it ain't much of a fight really, not the way the dogs fight. They just keep on biting the badger, hanging onto its neck and ears, four to one. I've seen it.'

Amos's features were frozen in shock, as Seth developed his tale.

'I were no more than a nipper. I didn't know what I were going to see, but I tell you I've never forgotten it. The old badger kept his head right down, tried to nip back at the dogs, but it couldn't move in the trench. When it got too dull, the fight, they pulled off the dogs and someone threw a brick at him to make him get up.'

'Did he?' Amos managed.

'Aye, it must have gone on for over an hour and then the badger were dead, just lying there. The dogs knew because they stopped attacking. That were it. We all went home again.'

'But why?'

'Money.'

'What sort of man wants to look at a thing like that?' said Henry. 'I'm going to ring the police.'

Seth took over badger duty after that, though it was some time before the baiters returned. He was sat on guard, his arms wrapped around him to keep warm, when he heard the first sound of dogs barking and yelping. It was an almost identical scene to the one Henry had described, the same dark montage, punctuated by occasional flashes of torchlight as the baiters arrived. Three, four figures with half a dozen dogs. They cast their nets over the sett entrances and drove their shovels into the ground. Then a sack came into the torchlight, with something wriggling inside it.

Seth bellowed at them in rage and loosed off a shot over their heads. The barking intensified, shouts of anger and alarm. Then someone came up behind the old gamekeeper and smacked him hard on the head with a shovel. When Seth came to, he tried to struggle to his feet, which was when the boots started going in. Seth groaned and wailed in agony until an old man approached the group and said, 'That's enough,' and the kicking stopped. Then he had added, 'Keep digging. I want the cubs too.'

The impact of NY Estates on the traditional way of life in Beckindale was felt immediately in new profit-orientated farming methods made possible by a revolution in science.

One evening, soon after the arrival of Trevor Thatcher, when Seth was on his way back from an illegal cull of two pheasants in Verney's woods, a partridge in Top Twenty, and a hare which he had caught in a noose on a slope nearby, Seth had spotted a fire in NY's Kimber barn and called the fire brigade.

There was a suspicion of foul play, but more worrying was the discovery that the barn was packed with Dichlobenil, a dangerous chemical. Farming with chemicals to speed up the natural processes of the soil was daily practice at NY. But the sheer quantity of the stuff at Kimber barn caused Beckindalers surprise. Then Joe discovered a problem at Peter Vine's trout farm above Leyburn, when he was out walking with a friend.

Earlier, Emmerdale nearly took a financial interest in the fish farm after Henry had agreed to keep an eye on the place while Peter was away. But in the end, Henry and the Sugdens had not become involved.

Now, as Joe looked into the great tanks, he saw the fish floating dead on the surface of the water and further analysis showed that the whole property was contaminated . . . with Dichlobenil. The poisons had worked their way through drainage systems and the soil from the Home Farm Estate, following the dowsing of the fire at Kimber barn.

Henry was quick to spot connections between events since NY had come on the scene and what they implied.

'Everything in Beckindale is changing,' Henry said, 'Nellie Radcliffe's cottage, that could never have happened when Mr Verney was in charge. And this irresponsible use of chemicals – he'd never have had them on his land, or certainly not in the quantities that caused a danger . . . Don't you see? . . . it's all part of . . . of something like a pattern . . .'

NY's targets for change were both the people and

NY Estates turned Seth Armstrong (pictured above with Bruce Westrop) from poacher to gamekeeper and brought him in line.

the land, the two parties in the relationship which underscored the whole culture of the Dales.

The pattern, once it had been set, was self-replicating. One day Henry found three pigeons dead on the ground. Not shot – plump birds, unaccountably lifeless. Then a fox was seen walking, dazed, and a picture began to emerge of a countryside in regression. This time it was Ernie Tully, who had used a chemical called Enodrin.

Joe Sugden looked into the kaleidoscope of change and opted to follow NY's more optimistic interpretation of the pattern emerging. Joe knew firsthand the drudgery of scratching a living at Emmerdale, and the big changes were an exciting opportunity. Joe

To NY Estates, hedgerows which had been in place for hundreds of years were nothing more than a waste of arable land.

even travelled to America to see how best to develop a new high-yeild strategy for Emmerdale.

NY was quick to win other recruits. Thatcher converted Seth from poacher to gamekeeper. It was the cleverest piece of NY strategy that he ever devised.

Others fought back. 'This is the Countryside Action Team,' the caller growled down the phone line to the surprised landlord of the Woolpack. 'C.A.T. for short. You want a story for your paper? We set fire to the barn. And there will be more action to protect the environment . . . The fire last night was a warning to NY Estates to stop wrecking our countryside. Our countryside ain't up for grabs by greedy money-makers.'

Beckindale's conservationists seemed at first sight an unlikely pair. One of them, Poor Ocker, so named after his ragged clothes, was barely three years out of school but already a drifter. Self-tutored in country matters since a child, he could tell things about Beckindale that many of its inhabitants might see but never notice. He could, for example, have told Henry, the great birdwatcher, where a wheatear was nesting on Emmerdale land or where Nellie's barn owl flew in its dusk-to-dawn sorties from the tower of St Mary's, or where on Grey Top Henry might see his favourite peregrine falcon.

People rarely spoke or listened to Poor. Only his friend Smarty Garrett gave him the time of day and the occasional lift on his Yamaha bike, which did little to recommend him to the rest of Beckindale.

When Poor spoke to Bruce Westrop, who had taken over from Thatcher at the NY helm, he was ripping out a hedgerow, which had separated two fields for more than 500 years. Poor knew how long by the number of different species of wood in the hedge, and he knew what species of bird had made the hedgerow their home.

'There was two linnet families, goldfinches and hedge- sparrows got a living outa that hedge. To say nothing of an owl as went along every evening so's you could set your watch by it. A lot o' stoats in it too. And at the far end, where it crossed rise, one of the few badger sets left in the county.'

Balance that against a little land gained and time saved by ploughing, sowing and harvesting one big field rather than two smaller ones. But it wasn't that easy an argument. NY Estates were the main employer in the area. Farming in the old way

was no longer profitable. It hadn't been for many years.

Somewhere deeper down in the steaming, bubbling cultural stew, Amos was doing his bit to thicken the traditional recipe. He had announced to Seth that he was planning 'to help win the battle against tinned and frozen food', the retail revolution which was leading farming by its nose into the 21st century. He had decided to apply for an allotment.

Seth agreed at once to have a word with a friend of his on the allotment committee to ensure that Amos's application received priority. Amos, so puffed up with self-importance by his newfound Greenness, failed to spot the twinkle in Seth's eye when he told him that a certain Mrs Bainwood's plot had recently fallen free.

Nor did Amos catch on when he passed Seth's potting shed on the way to see the plot. Though he might have done, for behind the door sat Sam and Seth almost rocking it with mirth at what had been earmarked for him.

Mrs Bainwood, it transpired, had been unable to dig her plot for eighteen months due to a progressive arthritic condition. Amos found himself tenant of the worst, most weed-ravaged site Beckindale had to offer.

Furious, but determined to hit back, Amos announced to Seth and Sam that he intended to operate in direct competition with them in the marrow class at the next horticultural show.

The shenanegans and dirty tricks which ensued culminated in Amos producing a vegetable, which in size and weight looked good enough to challenge anything his two competitors might have grown. But in the end justice was seen to be done and Seth, Sam and Amos all came joint second to the more honest endeavour of . . . Nellie Ratcliffe.

In 1980, when Jack Sugden returned to Emmerdale for good, determined to give up writing and return to farming, Sam scoffed at the idea – 'Machinery, chemicals, artificial insemination, it's all new since you used to help your dad.'

But that wasn't the half of it. Sixteen years as a

With expediency in farming came a similar revolution in the marketplace. Amos (left) joined battle against convenience foods on the Beckindale allotments, but Seth saddled Amos with the most weed-ravaged allotment on offer.

The marrow competition was hotly contested between Sam, Seth and Amos, but despite the shenanegans they came second to Nellie Ratcliffe.

writer had turned Jack soft and it wasn't long before Annie was complaining that he wasn't pulling his weight. The trouble with Jack was not just a physical one or his lack of knowledge of modern farming methods. Jack's conversion was all in the mind. He understood the value of Emmerdale as a writer might. He could describe it, but as yet he couldn't live it.

Joe, now back from the USA, pinpointed the problem when he and Sam came upon Jack waltzing his tractor to and fro, practising for the ploughing competition at the Loudwick Show. They laughed to themselves as they leaned on the gate and studied his efforts, and when Jack came alongside, Joe remarked, 'Very artistic, is that. I hear tell they're on to it in California . . . Landscape Art. They go out with ploughs and bulldozers and that, draw designs on the ground, circles and diamonds and so on.'

Joe's trip to the big wheat fields of America had brought him home determined to modernise methods at Emmerdale, and when he voiced his enthusiasm to Richard Anstey, the third manager of NY Estates, Anstey surprised him with an offer to run three of NY's farms covering an area three times the size of Emmerdale.

It was an astonishing offer, but Anstey was nobody's fool. He could see which way Joe had opted to go. NY could provide more funding and potential than a hill farm like Emmerdale ever could. Jack was home and wanted to farm. Joe wouldn't find it easy to settle into a working relationship as boss over a brother eight years his senior.

But at the back of his mind Joe worried that his decision to join Anstey was about more than these things, and he asked his mother for advice.

'When you were a young boy, Joe,' she reminded him, 'you made up your own mind to do a thing and did it without asking. I watched you do some things I thought were right daft, but I left you to it. It's the only way he'll learn, I thought . . .'

Annie knew the burden of the decision better than Joe. 'We'll never starve,' she reassured him, 'not while Matt's here to see to things and I've my health and strength, not forgetting Henry and his financial advice. This is summat you'll have to study out for yourself . . . I'll not make up your mind for you.'

Anstey pressed his invitation home with a guided tour of NY Estates in a spanking new Japanese 4-wheel drive, and before long there was no doubt

Joe and Jack in 1980. The different paths the brothers took after Jack's return to Emmerdale placed them on opposing sides in the battle being fought on every front for the future of Beckindale.

what Joe's decision would be. He had worked Emmerdale for a decade and never dreamed of reaping the rewards Anstey was talking about.

Soon after Jack took over from Joe at Emmerdale, he showed his inexperience by being conned by a dealer at Hotten market, who saddled him with two heifers intended as additions to Joe's prize pedigree Friesian dairy herd, but which died of salmonella. The disease threatened the whole herd.

Then, unaccustomed to the rigours of farm life, Jack pulled a muscle in his back and took five days off with Pat Merrick in Scarborough. He would eventually marry her, even though the vicar of Beckindale, now one Donald Hinton, refused to perform the ceremony because of course Pat was a divorcee. Just retribution, perhaps, for the bother Jack had caused Edward Ruskin all those years earlier. Meanwhile, Matt was turning increasingly sour at the extra burden he now had to shoulder with his new boss not pulling his weight. And Henry was increasingly concerned about the worsening accounts at Emmerdale.

On his return with Pat from the east coast, Jack delivered his strategy for the future. It couldn't have been more different to Joe's at NY, or worse news to Henry's ears.

Jack didn't want to be in the farming business like his brother, he wanted to be a farmer. As NY's farm manager, Joe was increasingly involved in working out wage packets, looking after tax and social security deductions, negotiating with unions who were demanding special rates for stockmen handling meat-enhancing hormones. For Jack, NY was what farming should not be – 'It's turning into a monster,' he said, 'destroying the country again, just as the first Industrial Revolution did. The first time all the people were driven into the towns. This time all the vitality is being drained away into ledgers and computers.'

Jack wanted to return Emmerdale to lea farming, growing a crop for a year but instead of grazing it, leaving it and ploughing it back in at the end of the next year. That way nitrogen would be sourced in the soil naturally rather than with chemical fertiliser – the 'robber economy', as Jack called it. 'In the end you just decrease the productivity of the land or else you pay more and more for fertilisers so that you eat into your profits . . . What's the point of robbing the

soil, putting nitrates into it that run off into the stream.'

When Matt pointed out that Joe and Henry were unlikely to agree, Jack replied simply that 'Joe can only see things the way NY Estates have taught him.'

The division between the Sugden brothers on farming methods represented the battle being fought on every front for the future of Emmerdale, social, economic, and environmental.

Jack's whole-earth policy would be claimed by Joe to be rooted in the past. Was it romantic to believe that Jack could ignore the scientific revolution in farming and still service a market? Would his ideas, as Henry feared, finally pull Emmerdale crashing down?

For purist Jack, even the market was suspect. In 1986, when Jackie, Jack's son born illegitimately to Pat Merrick during his first flight from Emmerdale, was working at the farm, the boy tried to impress his father by arranging for a meat buyer from Byrites, a

Seth showing Jackie Merrick how to handle a ferret. Jack's revelation that he and not Tom Merrick was Jackie's father had caused serious problems between father and son only resolved in 1985, the year before Jack's rejection of Jackie's Byrites deal, which made it all the more sensitive an issue.

supermarket chain, to visit the farm and look over 150 of Matt's lambs. Soames from Byrites had been struck by the quality of Matt's prize-winning ewes and had offered to take 30 lambs a week for a month. If they sold well he would be back to negotiate a longterm contract. It was a wonderful deal, won in the face of competition with NY Estates. But Jack, relentless even in the minutiae of his opposition to the pattern of progress, wasn't happy with it. Jack was stubbornly opposed to making even the smallest concessions to a market economy based on quantity rather than quality. For, despite its promise of profits, he believed that it threatened the very foundations of the rural culture to which he was now committed to protecting.

As before, Jack was an immoveable force. And as before, whatever you thought of his convictions, you couldn't fault him for his honesty and persistence.

Against all the odds, and with a split between the Sugden brothers in real danger of becoming terminal,

In the Beckindale production of Jack and the Beanstalk in 1978, Amos as Dame Margery, seen here spanking Dolly Acaster as Jack, while Joe looks on appreciatively, was not alone in tempting the audience to look below the surface performance.

Henry let a qualified version of Jack's plans for organic farming at Emmerdale go through.

In the Beckindale pantomime, *Jack and the Beanstalk*, in 1978, there had been a telling representation of what Jack now feared was on the cards for the village, perhaps the whole of rural England.

As ever, the panto brought the best out of everyone in the village. Amos accepted the part of panto Dame, Margery by name, and caused only one production hiccup, when he refused to shave off his outlandish sideburns. Later he suggested a compromise – covering them with pink sticking plaster, which led Joe to remark that it might be advisable not to be around when he tried to pull it off.

As Dame Margery, Amos revealed more of his true self even than his real life persona did, but he was not alone in tempting the audience to look below the surface performance.

From the wings, Sam Pearson had the job of pulling the beanstalk from its seed beginnings on stage high up into the proscenium (the Giant's castle, where the hen laid the golden eggs). On the night, to the great amusement of all but Sam, the drawstring broke and the beanstalk came crashing to the ground.

The collapse of the beanstalk, the means to the fictional Jack's golden destiny, occurred at a telling moment in the history of the village, the same year as NY Estates took over and the whole controversy about farming the modern way began.

Sam, whose farm labourer hands were pulling the traditional beanstalk to fruition, shared his grandson Jack's deep concern about hands-off farming with chemicals. But both were swimming against the tide.

As his opposition to Joe and Kathy had showed, Sam was equally concerned about the parallel social revolution in Beckindale, which he saw as part of the new pattern, which spelled the collapse of the way of life he'd been brought up in.

After his death in 1984, some younger people would remember Sam as a crusty old so-and-so. But as far as he was concerned, the years since Jacob's death in 1972 amounted to a complete cultural upheaval in the rural community.

For Sam it had been simple. His society was made up of a series of concentric circles radiating outwards like the ever-increasing ripples in a pond disturbed by a stone. God lay in the centre. He was the stone, the original cause of the disturbance called life. The rippling circles He had created were, from small to large, family, village, region, nation, the world.

But by the time of Sam's death it was all changing. God was no longer in the centre of the picture. The land had come under fire from the scientific revolution in farming, and, with the blurring of boundaries between village, nation and the world by the communications revolution, Sam's culture was being replaced by a competitive, global, 'culture of self', its value measured in wealth.

When Sam died it was truly the end of an era. But he didn't die an unhappy man, for his death followed his first prize pumpkin win at the village show.

Loyalty to Beckindale, the Beckindale he knew and had long enjoyed in the company of Annie, Amos, Seth and latterly Henry, was all that mattered, and at the last he had been richly rewarded for it in his own terms.

Two years earlier, in March 1982, Alan Turner had moved to Beckindale as NY Estates Manager, beating Joe to the job. He showed himself wholly ill-equipped for the task, driving Joe mad with his disorganisation, laziness and sleight of hand, and upsetting two of the four secretaries he got through in a year by his unwanted advances.

But in the first week of Turner's new appointment, Joe himself came unstuck. He had taken it upon himself to book a helicopter for a crop spraying job on the Estate and since the fields for spraying were close to Emmerdale he suggested a free going-over of some of Emmerdale's pasture. Matt had agreed but didn't bother to tell Jack about the plan or to keep his Friesians clear of the area because Jack had already told Matt that he planned to bring them down closer to the farm. Unfortunately, although the Friesians were brought in, Jack had only moved them one field closer to the farm, right into the path of the helicopter. The aircraft caused a stampede, one of his heifers was killed and two others aborted. It was a costly mistake. Jack accused Turner, who then faced Joe with the folly of his deal with Matt, saying that it was as good as putting his hand in the till. The rumpus eventually subsided when it was proven that the pilot had been careless, but the incident highlighted yet again the immediate physical danger inherent in NY's new methods.

Under Turner's continuing mismanagement, NY business suffered and events came to a head when he and Joe, as manager of Home Farm, received a visit from two executives from Head Office. Turner, while showing one of them around, left open the farrowing house door. It had been late evening. Turner, as usual, was well-oiled. But as night fell, the temperature outside plummeted and by morning twelve piglets had died. It was the last straw as far as Joe was concerned and he gave Turner a piece of his mind, 'Alan, it's time you and I had a heart-to-heart . . . I want to tell you straight out and honest, that I don't like the way the estate is run.'

'Let me tell you, Joe,' Turner puffed, 'I've got a lot of experience . . .'

' . . . of wriggling out of corners you got yourself into by your lack of grip,' Joe concluded.

In the end, Turner would sign his own demotion, firstly by failing to report the farrowing house incident and secondly by deliberately withholding from Head Office a report written by Joe following a course he had attended in Scotland. In it Joe had recommended that NY move from milk to beef production, and it turned out to be crucial to NY policy. When Head Office discovered all that had been going on, much of the business was taken out of Turner's hands, and Joe was posted to a key position at NY's beef ranch in France to breed Charollais, with the promise that when he had completed the assignment he would find himself in a senior position in NY UK.

While Joe was away, Turner gave up drinking and harassing his secretaries and was reconciled with his wife, Jill, who took it upon himself to appoint one Caroline Bates as her husband's new assistant.

In March 1982, Alan Turner rode in as the new manager of NY Estates, beating Joe to the job.

Disorganised, lazy and abrasive, Alan Turner drove Joe mad at Home Farm.

Caroline Bates and Alan Turner. She was the major influence in the tempering of Alan's abrasive personality.

Caroline was a divorcee, with two children, Kathy and Nick, a no-nonsense woman who organised Turner's work-life and helped him through various scrapes in his personal life too. But her appointment turned out not to be a good move for Jill because Alan Turner was smitten by Caroline. In fact, for one often comical reason or another, Caroline and Alan didn't make it together until five years later and their plans for marriage were wrecked by Caroline's interfering mother, who eventually enticed her to Scarborough to look after her. Nevertheless, over the years, Caroline did much to soften the edges of Alan's abrasive character and help integrate him into the Beckindale community.

In 1985, Turner again came into the firing line for careless use of chemicals. This time children were hospitalised after the wind had carried the spray. The weather had been wrong for it, dangerously changeable, and the carry suggested also that it had been incorrectly diluted. Turner was already an unpopular figure in the village, and following a dangerous driving incident earlier in the year, in which Jackie was despatched to the intensive care unit with a broken leg and severe concussion, he became an outcast even in the NY Social Club. That summer, on the day of the Beckindale village fête, Amos had a front page article in the Hotten Courier about the dangerous spraying.

When Turner saw it, he was furious – 'Ah, the scribbler of Beckindale,' he greeted Amos, after parking the NY show caravan on the Woolpack forecourt, 'I didn't know you were a master of fiction as well as a small time reporter.'

He threatened Amos with a suit for slander, but was soon besieged by angry people, particular interest being shown in him by Seth's donkey, which had been giving rides to children at the fete and had escaped its handler.

As Turner backed away from the hordes, maintaining his innocence over the spraying incident, the donkey nuzzled him into the van, positioning itself over the NY promotional video, before leaving an appropriately pungent calling card on the caravan floor.

The donkey then proceeded to upset a beehive and release a swarm of indignant bees, which pursued

What Seth's donkey did expressed most succinctly what the people of Beckindale thought of Alan Turner and NY Estates.

Amos as he ran for his life through the village, shout-ing, 'Take cover!' The scene was like a fast forward of a film of the *Pied Piper of Hamlyn*, the crowd following in Amos's wake to the village pond, where he threw himself into its dank depths. Only when he emerged, soaked and stricken, did the landlord realise that the crowd had been trying to tell him that the bees had long ago taken refuge in a tree.

Joe returned from France the following year, in 1986, and was given regional responsibility at NY Estates, much to Turner's resentment. And the dif-ferences between Joe and Jack surfaced once more too.

Joe set his sights on Hotten market, believing it was a natural progression for NY to get into the marketing arm of the farming industry. Hotten Mar-ket operated a livestock market and a parallel farm estate agency and property auction room. Sandie Merrick, Jack's stepdaughter, had returned from Aberdeen two years earlier and was auctioneer at

Hotten Market became an unpopular target of Joe's business strategy for NY Estates to gain ever tighter control over farmers in the area.

Sandie Merrick returned to Beckindale from Aberdeen in 1984 and became auctioneer at Hotten Market.

the market.

Both Jack and Henry voiced local farmers' concern about the increased power Joe's move gave NY Estates over independents in the industry, and there was some suspicion in Jack's mind about whether Golding, the market's owner for the past fifty years, had been pressured into the sale by Joe.

Henry told Golding that the sale meant that henceforth NY would control both the farming and marketing interests of many independent farmers in the area. Golding replied that he wasn't changing his mind, and Henry sold his shares in NY as a personal protest.

Under Joe's management, the tentacles of NY's power seemed to be spreading into other areas too. Amos was having problems getting Tyler, the editor of the Hotten Courier, to print people's doubts about NY's purchase of the market. It was beginning to look as if NY had the whole place wrapped up. At this stage, Turner, sensing the drift of opinion, added his own two pennyworth at his new boss's expense – 'We dominate this area; there is no real competition, Joe. Surely you can see that. Do we really need to dominate any more than we do already?'

Joe's reaction made his own position patently clear: 'All right, but it has to be said, Alan, though I don't like saying it, this deal's the best business transaction I've ever negotiated. It was enough to turn a bloke's head when I heard Meadows' compliments when I put him on the train. If he'd heard you rabbiting on about local farmers' interests he'd have had you for being disloyal to the company.'

Turner replied, 'I'm not being disloyal. Isn't it in the best interests of NY Estates if we are seen to be acting morally in the best interests of the community . . . It's getting to be too much in too few hands.'

Joe was developing something of a ruthless streak and when he began directing it at a farmer regarded by Annie as one of their own, it again became clear just how far Joe had strayed.

Clifford Longthorn had fallen behind on the rent for his farm, and NY management at headquarters had ordered Turner to get him out and locate their new poultry battery units on his land. Turner was not at all happy about it and confided in Mrs Bates. Joe told him to follow Head Office orders. But again,

Turner refused.

'And if I tell you you've got to do it?' Joe, his immediate boss, asked.

'Tell me what you like, but I'm not doing it . . . I'm well aware of what people think of me round here. If I serve notice on Clifford Longthorn I might as well serve one on myself. It'll have the same effect because after that I wouldn't get a drink in a village puddle, let alone the Woolpack or the Malt Shovel. I'll be ostracised and you know it.'

The issue obviously had dire ramifications for the Longthorn family and Annie took it up with Joe, spelling out to her son what had once been second nature to him.

'The Longthorns have been in this Dale more years than the Sugdens!' she exclaimed.

'Aye, I know.' Joe said sheepishly.

'Well why, Joe?'

'Head office decided they wanted the land back . . .' As far as Joe was concerned, Longthorn had gone bust anyway, sticking to dairy because that's what he'd always done, 'closing the door in your face when you try giving him help . . . How can you hold a man's hand when he's already gone under?'

'They're asking you to throw out a man you've known all your life,' Annie replied, 'Is this the sort of job you've got, Joe? Is this the sort of thing they're going to make you do? I don't want you in a job like that, Joe, not one that makes it difficult for you to sleep at night.'

But Joe was already in the job, up to his neck one might say, and it had changed him, not just in terms of farming, but as this episode showed, in terms of life. You couldn't be two people at the same time. The job and the man were one in farming, as they'd always been.

One side effect of the 'winner-takes-all' philosophy, which seemed to be taking over everywhere in the 1980s, was a growing incidence of people taking a short cut to success through crime.

Eric Pollard's criminal career within the environs of Beckindale, which would encompass the swindling of nearly everyone in the village, began two years after he was appointed manager of Hotten Market by NY Estates in 1986.

In 1988, Sandie Merrick's assistant, Miss Spencer, reported an item, known as the Lalique glass, missing from one of the lots in a house clearance auction. Sandie took her to Eric, who dismissed it as a lot of nonsense. But later Sandie remembered seeing the glass too, and was amazed when Eric rebuffed her again, this time saying that her refusal to let the matter rest was yet another example of why their relationship was so strained.

Then Sandie noticed the odd discrepancy in the auction sales ledger and when she approached Pollard about it, again he was dismissive and sent her out to buy some coffee. On her way, she passed a shop run by an antique dealer friend of Pollard, and she was astonished to see on show what she was convinced was the missing glass.

Something was going on, Sandie was sure of that. Eric began turning up for work looking dischevelled and smelling of alcohol. Even more unnervingly, he began to congratulate her on her work as auctioneer. Then he began spending the occasional night in the office, tidying himself up before Sandie arrived.

When the accounts were inspected, the discrepancies had been rectified. Coincidentally Eric had sold his car to release some cash. When finally he resigned from the job (before he was pushed), he accused Sandie of bringing him down, and when subsequently Sandie got the job of running the office in his place, she had a strange feeling that she had not heard the last of him.

Sandie was living at Mill Cottage at the time with a builder called Phil Pearce. She had bought it from Joe the same year. One evening while she was home alone, listening to music, the power suddenly went off.

Fancying she had seen a figure prowling around outside she reached for the phone and dialled 999, but as she did so the phone was snatched from her hand. It was Pollard, drunk. He proceeded to pour out his resentment about her shopping him and threatened to make Sandie pay for ruining his life.

But Eric Pollard was never a physically dangerous man, more of a weak one, a weasel with no teeth when it came to a real bite. Whenever possible he got other people to do his dirty work for him. Sandie was his match, and when the tirade was over, she gave him a lift home.

Meanwhile the differences between the two Sugden brothers were coming to a head.

NY Estates had learned that the Government proposed to test Pencross Fell as a dumping site for

Eric Pollard, an expression of the temptation in us all to take a short cut to success, was appointed manager of Hotten Market in 1986.

Pollard threatened to make Sandie pay for ruining his life.

nuclear waste. Turner raised the issue with Joe, who immediately battoned down the hatches and said there was no point ringing alarm bells in people's minds until plans reached a more definite stage.

News of the proposals finally broke in the newspapers, and the next day a notice was posted outside Beckindale village hall advertising a public meeting.

When Jack discovered that Joe and Alan Turner had had prior knowledge of the proposals he warned them that NY would have to answer for any involvement they had in the scheme. Annie took Joe aside and told him that she didn't want the family divided over the issue, and he promised that he would try to attend the public meeting.

When Mr Bailey, a representative from the nuclear industry, turned up to address the crowded village hall, Jack confronted him. Jack and a number of other villagers, in particular Archie Brooks, were adamant that no quarter should be given.

But Bailey was adept at reassuring Matt and Dolly when they asked questions, and Mrs Harriet Ridgley-Jones, Beckindale's MP, urged people to let tests be carried out at Pencross Fell and then listen to the results before making up their minds. Then, to jeers from Jack and others, she told them that she would not be voting against the proposals in Parliament, and the vicar, Donald Hinton, rounded off the meeting by making it clear on behalf of the village that the slightest degree of risk was unacceptable. Jack was furious to hear Ridgley-Jones publicly describe the meeting as dignified, and dismissed the whole thing as being far too full of restraint.

Henry tried to agree a common strategy in a second meeting held at the Woolpack, spelling out the problem with almost Churchillian fervour, 'We want to fight the proposals that's clear enough, but who to lobby, who to go to for advice, how to organise the massive effort that will be involved in a long and intense campaign. These are the decisions we have to make . . . The effort will be massive, the campaign will be long and tedious at times and doubtless full of frustration.'

Jack then made an impassioned plea against Hinton's call for restraint – 'My reason is in the families, in the farm, in the fields and the crops and the animals, and my argument is in my son, in the children and the young people of Beckindale. Whatever the motives, these people are our enemies, the ene-

Jack confronted Mr Bailey and made it clear that Beckindale's answer was 'No!'

mies of our community. Our only position is "No!", our only reason is "No!", our only argument is "No!" For a thousand years the church has stood in Beckindale. Donald, would you say that the life that's been lived here all those generations is threatened? Don't let's pretend it's all about discussion. What are we saying? If they can prove our rocks are as solid as they say, bring on the low level waste, we'll all be happy, reason has won the day? You tell that to farmers in the Dale with newborn lambs registering on Geiger counters. Our only course is to fight, make Beckindale a place they can't come to at all, to test, to do one damn thing. That's what we have to believe. Everyone who lives here. And that means everyone!'

At that moment Joe came in, and there was a hush. When Jack called over to him – 'You're either with us or . . .' – it sounded like a call he had long been wanting to make to his brother.

But Joe stood his ground. ' . . .Or if I don't want to block the streets with burning tractors or chain myself to mine shafts on Pencross Fell, I'm against you? You're going to find a lot of people against you by that measure, Jack. Our family's knocked around these parts for not far off a thousand years. I've no desire for it not to be for another thousand years. But a few things have changed since we arrived . . . If I'm not sure where the power to run the milking machines is coming from in the 21st century, I don't think that makes me an enemy of this village. I might have some views on wind power and wave power and all the rest of it, but if it is I can't say dump it anywhere but here. I don't want it here, but I can't just turn my back on the real world and put up a barricade.'

Both brothers were arguing their case for the future of Beckindale, but it could have been for the world. Later, Joe would say, 'The future's already here, it's staring us in the face. Running away from it won't help. It's here and it includes nuclear power. Time we

News that the Government proposed to test Pencross Fell as a dumping site for nuclear waste galvanised the village into opposition and brought the differences between the Sugden brothers to a head.

were ready. Your way we get the worst of both worlds. No nuclear power of our own, but still the risk of suffering from an accident at some other country's nuclear power station.'

In the end, Jack got the backing he wanted from the meeting and the village moved remorselessly to an active campaign. Placards were made for a demonstration to coincide with Bailey's visit the following day, and when he arrived, his placid mood, encouraged by his earlier success, was at once upset by the banner-waving reception committee outside the village hall.

Resigned rather than angry, Bailey accompanied Hinton inside, where he delivered an intricate scientific monologue about nuclear waste. Then, suddenly, a crudely made coffin decorated with nuclear symbols appeared in their midst, and the packed hall rose

Henceforth the battle for Beckindale's future would be fought on the ground. Here Jackie makes his point while Kathy Bates, Nick Bates, Archie Brooks and Beckindale's vicar, the Reverend Donald Hinton, look on.

in cheers and laughter as Archie Brooks emerged from inside it through clouds of smoke in a skeleton suit. Bailey was left with no choice but to abandon the meeting.

War had been declared. The next battle would be fought on the ground. It was a Sunday and the people of Beckindale had flocked to hear what Hinton would have to say. Then, part way through the service, Archie (with Seth the campaigners' eyes and ears) interrupted it to announce that the contractors' convoy had arrived and was making for Pencross Fell.

When the campaigners arrived on the fell, an angry exchange with Police Sergeant MacArthur and the contractors led to two arrests. But the result was a succesful disruption of the work. The following day, when the convoy returned, it came upon Jack's tractor, which had apparently broken down on a bend in the road. Starting up another road, it met a flock of sheep being driven down towards them by Matt. There were lookouts in sight of all the lanes leading to the top. Jock McDonald had a tipper trailer full of manure, which he dropped onto a third approach, and once again, the convoy turned back. But then, while everyone celebrated in the Woolpack, McDonald's manure was shifted and the convoy finally arrived at its destination.

And so it went on, with the non-stop campaign directed now against the site itself, farmers teaming up with Jack to cut huge holes in the fence and Sgt MacArthur doing his best to keep matters within the law. But such was the fervour in Jack's army of supporters that Matt was issued with an injunction to keep him away from the fell and eventually Jack himself was arrested and taken to Armley jail. There, he discovered that plans for the dump had already been scrapped.

Meanwhile, NY Estates had got itself got into financial difficulties and the workforce went on strike. It began to look as if the promise of science would not be fulfilled, at least in Beckindale, and Joe discovered that it wasn't as easy to pull in the horns of an operation as big as NY, as once it had been at Emmerdale.

At least hard times did finally bring Joe and Alan Turner into closer harmony for a while. In January 1988 they put together a package to buy the Home Farm Estate from NY. Their offer was accepted. Unfortunately, eight months later, Turner reverted to type and without even discussing the matter with Joe, sold his shares to Denis Rigg, a ruthless businessman who had been pressuring local farmers to sell their land so that his company could convert the landscape into a quarry.

Rigg had teamed up with Eric Pollard, who, since leaving Hotten Market, had set up his own antiques business and hatched a plan to steal some ornate fireplaces from Home Farm.

He had stolen the keys to the Hall from Caroline Bates's handbag and had managed to persuade Sandie Merrick's boyfriend, Phil Pearce, to do the dirty work on the ground, while he kept Turner and Mrs Bates occupied, carol singing with the rest of the village. But when Phil let himself in to Home Farm he found the fires lit and had to use a fire extinguisher to dowse them, before ripping out the fireplaces and dumping them in a disused barn. The heist was initially successful, but when Phil was moving the fireplaces to sell them, he was arrested.

Pollard's great strength was an extraordinary ability to live virtually unscathed in the community on which he preyed. It was a conman's strength. Later he would be described by someone who was not herself averse to a bit of petty crime, as a gentleman, and Eric could be suave and charming when he wanted to be (to the ladies especially when there was something to

NY Estate workers had begun to voice their grievances to Alan Turner and went out on strike. It looked as if the revolution in farming had not after all taken hold in Beckindale.

Nick Bates with Archie Brooks on the wall outside Mrs Bates's cottage in 1988.

be gained by it). He was certainly always the performer.

Incredibly, though he himself was put in prison, Phil Pearce didn't implicate Pollard. And when the police went looking for co-conspirators, Pollard pointed the finger at Sandie and Phil Pearce's friend, Nick Bates (Caroline's son), both of whom were innocent.

The year before, Nick Bates had been celebrated as a hero, when he had helped foil a raid on Beckindale's Post Office. What he had never admitted, however, was that he'd helped himself to some of the cash from the raid before it was retrieved by the police, and when the police came knocking at his door Nick's guilty conscience gave him away and he confessed to taking the money.

Pollard walked away scot-free. His talent for doing so was only matched by his ability to entice accomplices into his schemes, which had an almost Fagin-esque quality, as was shown in 1989, the year he teamed up with Denis Rigg.

Eric Pollard's talent for avoiding arrest was equal only to his ability to enlist willing accomplices.

'I want everything sold,' Rigg told Alan Turner, his right-hand man following his purchase of the Home Farm Estate. 'Land we don't need can be rented out. Barns can be sold for conversion. There's a million and one things to be done, Alan, so I suggest you get busy.'

Turner, his conscience already pricking him, refused to have any part in it, and Rigg told him, 'As long as you're my manager, you'll do as I say, Alan.'

It was overdue for Turner to take a stand, but he drew the line anyway: 'Not any more Denis, I've done your dirty work for too long.'

'Poor old Alan,' Pollard commented later, 'I must say I am surprised. I never thought noble gestures were quite his line . . . Now, what about the tenanted cottages? Done up they could fetch a fortune.'

Rigg told Pollard he'd need the cottages for his quarry workers, which indeed meant that he wanted the Home Farm tenants out. It also meant that

Pollard needed recruits. Who should he think of first, but gullible Nick Bates, whose mother had given Turner shelter after he was thrown out of Home Farm by Rigg. Caroline's cottage was leased from Home Farm.

Pollard approached Nick and suggested provocatively that the only reason his mother had her cottage at a low rent from Home Farm was that she used to have an affair with Turner. Nick replied rather angrily, 'Me mum pays a fair rent and there has never been anything between her and Turner.'

'I wouldn't waste your commendable loyalty on Alan Turner,' Pollard replied smoothly, 'He's yesterday's man and as I gather your mother has seen fit to throw him out, she obviously realised it. But having no protector will make life a little harder for her.'

'Is this a threat Pollard?' Nick demanded.

'Mr Pollard, Nick. Be very, very careful . . .as you may have overheard, I have the responsibility of making the Home Farm properties available for Denis Rigg's men. Now, I can either start with your mother's cottage or leave it till last. I don't mind which. It all depends on you.'

Fortunately for Caroline and the other tenants, Rigg's ownership of the Home Farm Estate didn't last long enough for his plans to go through. He was taken over by entrepreneur businessman Frank Tate.

Meanwhile, Turner, in partnership with Caroline Bates, had rented the fish and game farm from the Estate and once again the dangers of modern farming methods came to the fore. Alan had hired Seth Armstrong, who had been taken to hospital, stricken with a mystery virus. As ebullient as ever, Turner visited him in hospital and blamed Seth's drinking habits for his sickness, 'It's your whole damn lifestyle that's put you here.' But Seth and his doctors suspected otherwise. 'My lifestyle was fine when I

The driveway to Home Farm, where Pollard planned a burglary and got Phil Pearce to do the dirty work for him.

Alan Turner and Caroline Bates enjoying a less pressurised existence at the fish and game farm in 1990, with assistant Seth in the foreground, soon to be stricken with a mystery virus.

were a proper gamekeeper,' Seth countered, 'It were only since you made me a fish keeper that I got ill.' Turner dismissed it as coincidence, but Seth warned him, 'Doctor don't think so. He's been reet interested in where I work . . . You'll be getting a visit from health man, I bet.'

Later, when Zoe Tate, a trainee vet and daughter of the new owner of the Home Farm Estate, came to satisfy herself that there was no risk, she asked Turner about safeguards against run-off from the fields entering the fish tanks from the river, which fed them. 'If we sight any slurry in the river,' Turner reassured her, 'We cut off the inlet valves until its gone past the fish farm.'

'So it does happen,' Zoe mused.

'Yes, very rarely. But that's nothing to do with Seth. He's got a mild case of diarrhoea, which he's making a meal of . . . if you see what I mean.'

Zoe, although she barely knew Turner, immediately recognised in the man his inveterate tendency to push any problem under the carpet, 'You don't really care, do you?' she said rather coldly, 'So long as it doesn't land on your doorstep.' Her next stop was Emmerdale – the fish farm's feeder stream ran right through Emmerdale's land – where she asked Jack how he managed the farm slurry. Jack showed her the slurry pit. 'All the slurry from the mistel goes in here . . . When it's full, we pump it out and spread it on the fields . . . We're developing a beef herd now and extra cattle means extra slurry.'

'Is it possible that the excess could be leaking into the water course?' Zoe asked him.

'It's possible,' Jack conceded. 'In the winter we've got more beasts inside which means they're not spreading the muck on the fields themselves and it's difficult for us to get out muckspreading as often as we need . . .'

Meanwhile, back at Home Farm, Nick Bates, who now worked there as a gardener, was in a terrible state. He had discovered some of Frank Tate's much-prized coi-carp floating on the surface of his ornamental pond.

As Nick began to collect dead fish in a bucket with the idea of burying them somwhere on the farm, Frank Tate strode across the grass towards him and Nick, desperate to cover up what would almost certainly cost him his job, thrust a couple of the fish into his pocket. Apparently unsuspecting, Frank invited Nick for a drink in the Woolpack, and by the time they arrived Nick was a dithering wreck. Immediately he excused himself and repaired to the toilet, where he stuffed the dead fish into the bowl and pulled the chain, before returning to the bar even more relieved than he would normally be after a visit to the Gents.

A while later, Henry noticed that Amos was looking, well, a bit strained. 'You look like you've seen a ghost,' he said to his partner with some concern.

'Summat more mysterious than that Mr Wilks,' Amos said. 'Look -' and he held up a dead carp. 'That were in . . . facility!' Just as Amos had been preparing to sit on the toilet he had looked down and – 'they were looking back at me!'

Mystery indeed. Amos became convinced that he had happened upon some strange quirk in nature. 'It has been known to rain frogs, y'know,' he said to Henry. 'They get whipped up in whirling winds and come down miles away.'

'What's that got to do with dead carp in our Gents?' asked Henry.

'They're not like salmon are they? Swimming thousands of miles back to the place where they were born,' Amos mused. 'They might have got lost.'

'Took a left turn at Bradford sewage works instead of a right into the Pacific Ocean you mean?' Henry suggested.

Zoe's tests on the water at the fish farm proved positive, and she was convinced that it had something to do with Emmerdale's slurry pond.

Turner was relieved that blame, at least for the original cause of the problem, looked like being placed elsewhere, 'You mean I'm being poisoned by the Sugdens? Typical. I am very grateful for this information Miss Tate,' he said patronisingly.

Further tests confirmed that the same bacteria was present in Jack's cattle, sourced in a chemical slime-killer Jack had been using and had lent to Nick.

By 1989, some use of chemicals was inevitable, even by a man with Jack's principles and even if you managed to keep them away from plants and animals. Chemicals were as much a part of farming as chemical additives were of food. Joe was right, the

The Tate family, Frank, Kim, Chris and Zoe enjoy their first Christmas at Home Farm in 1989.

future was already with Beckindale. There could be no turning back.

But increasingly safeguards were coming into force. Whether it was the Green lobby or a balance of enlightened self-interest struck between scientists and politicians, or whether it was simply the result of experience, legislation brought compromise of a sort. For example, the use of steroids in the fattening of the beef herd had now been banned. Unfortunately, legislation was not always enough.

In 1990 Joe was back at Emmerdale and without reference to his elder brother, began injecting Emmerdale's calves with steroids. Jack was furious when he learned what he'd been up to, and his girlfriend Sarah Connolly (Pat had died three years earlier) did little to calm him down.

'This whole business about steroids has been blown up out of all proportion,' she said carelessly.

'You know about it do you?' he asked.

Sarah ran the mobile library until the service was

The danger of slurry and chemicals polluting Beckindale's watercourse was now a reality.

axed by Hotten Council later in the year. She had indeed informed herself.

'Yes,' she said, 'I read the articles in the library. When all's said and done the whole business is about protecting the European beef market against the Americans. They use steroids routinely, so let's ban them so that we can protect our poor farmers against competitive imports . . . I just hate to see the issues getting muddled by the muck and magic brigade.'

Jack was not about to be drawn into an argument with Sarah, which he knew would change nothing – 'And this from a woman who will kill for an organic bean sprout . . . Look, the bottom line is that it's against the law. OK the whole system strikes me

as pretty . . . you put nitrates on the field to get more grass to feed more cows, which you then make bigger with steroids, so all you end up with is low prices, a beef mountain and a nitrate problem.'

Despite his brother's protest, Joe insisted on taking the calves to market and, to his credit, Jack accompanied him because, as he put it, 'a. you're my brother even if you are a prat; b. it's a family business and if I'm going to get dumped on I'd like to be there to see it happen; c. I'm sick of Sarah nagging me about it, OK?'

At Hotten Market Joe was congratulated on the form of his calves. 'A lot of the blokes didn't have enough grass for grazing let alone silage. It's costing them a fortune in winter feed. Lucky if they get their money back some of them,' said the manager.

Understandably, Joe was slightly defensive: 'We've got the same problem.'

'You seem to have managed alright though, especially for sucklers. What's your secret?'

Jack moved swiftly in – 'Blood sacrifice under a full moon' – and brought the inquisition to a close.

Zoe Tate was walking round with the local vet, and the brothers noticed that they fell deep into converstaion when they came to the Emmerdale calves.

Nevertheless, all went well as bids were taken – 'Lot 263, also from the Emmerdale suckler herd. Five calves at 10 months. Who'll start me at £340? Bidding goes up in £5s until £360 when it goes up in £2s. . .'

'Stop clenching your fists.' Jack whispered to Joe.

His brother changed to folding his arms, 'She's looking again. They're talking about our animals.'

'There's no other animals around for them to talk about are there?' Jack said reassuringly.

'What are they saying?'

'I'm not a flaming lip reader. How should I know, he's probably chatting her up.'

' . . . £380, £380, sold Mr Blackmore.'

At 3pm, as the market emptied, Joe finally relaxed – 'Dammit, they've made it!'

It was a maturer Jack to whom Joe had come home to, family was now important to him too. He picked up on Joe's relief and suddenly they were like two small boys again. 'Do you remember that day we went and nicked all Mrs Hobson's plums off her tree.'

'I thought she was going to call the police,'

'So did I.'

'In fact you told me we'd probably spend the rest of our lives in prison.'

'Did I?'

But the following day there was a knock at the Emmerdale kitchen door. It was Henry Braithwaite, the Ministry of Agriculture, Fisheries and Food vet, who had attended the auction with Zoe. Braithwaite demanded to see Mr Sugden. 'Following a spot check at the abbertoir, those carcases originating from this farm have been impounded. Tests have been made and we strongly suspect an unauthorised use of

Where Frank Tate kept his prize coi-carp at Home Farm, and Nick Bates got himself into a muddle.

steroids.'

Joe was immediately testy – 'I hope you can prove that,' he said.

'Oh I think so Mr Sugden. Meanwhile we'll have to examine all your stock. May I take a look round?'

'Now just a minute . . .'

Jack intervened – 'You carry on Mr Braithwaite.'

The steroid business cost Emmerdale nigh on £10,000 and ruined their reputation at market. As a direct result, Joe had to put Demdyke up for sale. Afterwards, Jack tried his best to convince his brother to go into organic lamb farming, using market logic which Joe might understand. Joe's new suckling beef herd would take two years to

bring to market, whereas Jack's organic lamb would be ready within eighteen months. But Joe would have none of it.

Ironically it was businessman Frank Tate who suggested that Jack might have a point.

Joe met Frank Tate's wife first, the beautiful horsewoman, Kim. He had narrowly missed running into her in his car and, on discovering that they shared a love for horses, Kim had asked Joe to help exercise hers. Riding out on Home Farm land one day, she asked Joe whether he missed the place.

'In a way,' he admitted, 'but looking back I suppose I'm glad we got out when we did. The interest rates are really crippling now.'

'You couldn't make the place pay?' Kim asked.

'Well, I was in partnership with Alan Turner, it wasn't the best combination.'

'He held you back did he?'

'Yes, I like to think so. What about your husband?'

'What about him?'

'He's going to make the place pay is he?'

'I sincerely hope so,' Kim clearly had no doubt that Frank would. Joe then asked her about Frank's grazing land with his own beef suckler herd in mind.

Later, when she went over their conversation with her husband, Kim expressed annoyance at the way Joe had used her as a kind of go-between with Frank to get what he wanted for his herd. Kim could be a prickly customer. She was a woman who liked her own way and was not accustomed to being used as a means to anyone elses. 'I mean, did he think I wouldn't notice he was using me?' she said to Frank.

'Probably didn't care,' Frank replied. 'The Sugdens have been used to getting their own way around here for some time.'

When, finally, Joe and Frank discussed his idea, Frank made him pay for his mistake. 'Kim told me you've got plans for my land and I am flattered. But you are a farmer and I am a businessman, what can we possibly have in common?'

'Everything,' Joe said enthusiastically, thinking to himself that he and Frank were much of a breed. 'Farming is a business, why else do you think we

Left: Joe showing one of his calves in the auction arena at Hotten Market.

do it?'

Frank milked him outrageously, 'I thought farmers were romantics, scraping a living for love of the soil.'

'That's more my brother's line,' Joe replied. 'I'm after profit, not penury.'

Although Joe didn't realise it, he had just lost the deal.

Frank suggested an absurdly weighted, unacceptable profit arrangement, and then promptly contacted Jack.

Jack was intrigued by Frank's call and accepted his invitation to share with him his views on organic farming: 'If the rich countries don't change their lifestyles quite drastically pretty soon,' he began, 'this planet could be finished. Intensive farming produces lots of cheap food, but it pollutes and it is not always kind to animals. There are better ways of doing things.'

Frank smiled. Where there was division, there might be money to be made – 'I can see why you and your brother don't get on.'

'Oh we get on, most of the time,' Jack said, and Frank warmed to his approach, more guarded than his younger brother's.

'But if I read things right, you wouldn't mind taking a different course from him.'

'Oh no,' agreed Jack, 'I usually do.'

Frank then told him that there was land standing idle at Home Farm and he wanted someone to farm it for him. Would Jack be interested?

'I don't get it,' Jack said, who had already heard that Frank had pronounced that sheep farming was finished in the Dales. Indeed Frank had just persuaded Matt, the best sheep farmer in the area, to work in East Anglia. 'Now you're telling me you want to put sheep onto Home Farm.'

'Organic sheep, that's the difference. Organic food's a growth market.'

Had the market really come full circle? Could health fears about modern farming practices turn farming on its head? For the first time in Jack's life as a farmer, he had the backing of a no-holds-barred businessman. Henry had helped his schemes in the past but only for Annie's sake, to maintain a balance in the Sugden household. Frank was saying that there was, or would soon be, a viable market for what he wanted to do.

'Emmerdale's sheep must be half way organic already,' Frank Tate said to Jack.

'I've got 75 acres of set-aside pasture that's not been touched for two years,' Frank told him, 'That should be enough to satisfy the Soil Association, and Emmerdale's sheep must be half way organic anyway.'

'This year's lambs any road. If they were treated right, the lambs which they produce could certainly be officially organic.'

'So, you're interested.'

'Sure I'm interested, but I warn you I'm a purist. If I'm going to go organic I'm going to go 100% – no chemicals, no antibiotics, human slaughter, and no cutting corners over fattening or feed.'

'Organic lamb is viable in North Yorkshire. It's environmentally friendly . . . Tourists like seeing lambs jumping around,' Frank concluded.

Joe would be knocked sideways by the arrangement. Somewhere along the road, it now seemed

The beautiful horsewoman, Kim, had been Frank Tate's secretary until the death in 1984 of Frank's wife, Jean, from cancer.

that Joe had taken a wrong turning. But Frank Tate's coming to the village created anything but a return to a traditional way of life. The clue to his real plans lay not in his promise to Jack of profits from organic farming, but in that sentence of his, 'Tourists like seeing lambs jumping around.'

At a dinner for Alan Turner at Home Farm, he spelled it out more precisely. He asked Turner what he would think about his building a theme park – 'a funfair, boating lake, that sort of thing.'

Even Turner was aghast. 'I'd be appalled!' he said.

'Amos Brearly wouldn't,' replied Tate, sitting back in his chair. 'When the charas start turning up he'd do pretty well out of it.'

'I'm sure Amos would be firmly opposed to the idea,' said Turner, still reeling from the news.

'To increased profits? I doubt it . . .' laughed Tate.

'But it would ruin the character of the village,'

Turner protested.

'This part of the world needs a damn good shake-up,' Tate continued warming to his theme.

'You mean with museums and funfairs and car parks?' Turner still can't believe it isn't all a joke.

'It may surprise you,' Tate broke in, 'but that is the kind of thing that could save the Dales.'

'That's not my idea of conservation,' said Turner firmly.

'Your idea is leaving things as they are. That's what's been happening. Look at the Dales over the last 100 years. Loss of jobs, fewer farmers, there's no point preserving that.'

'But it's the countryside that wants preserving,' pleaded Turner, 'It shouldn't be developed the way you talk of.'

'But someone's got to pay for it. You can bet it won't be farmers and it won't be the government. What it needs is private enterprise of a kind this area hasn't see before.'

As it happened, Amos would not be benefiting from the charabancs of tourists turning up. For he would hand over the reins at the Woolpack to Alan Turner himself after suffering a heart attack at Annie's 70th birthday party. At the Woolpack, with Caroline, Alan would at last find some sort of peace with himself, but not before a real struggle to make the pub work. He would bring the Woolpack into the 20th century and turn the tap room into a restaurant, which would win prizes for gourmet cuisine. Then he would have the whole place redesigned and invite Ian Botham to open it officially.

But before Turner made his big move, and shortly after Tate had had his chat with Jack Sugden, the entrepreneur promoter announced his plans publicly and in detail to the press in a marquee erected for the purpose at Home Farm.

The assembled throng waited, some expectantly, others like Nick Bates, yawning or fingering press packs which earlier had been handed out by Kim. Then Frank Tate rose to his feet and delivered his plans for Emmerdale's future, as he saw it:

'I bought this house, Home Farm and the 650 acres that go with it for a number of reasons: to live in of course, to save it from the developer who wanted to excavate a quarry, but also to earn money from it. Now, how can I do that when none of my predecessors seems able to? Well, I can, I can make money, and benefit the local economy. The problem with the Dales is that profitable farming is in decline.'

Frank turned to refer to a large map of the area: 'There is a solution. In order to achieve many of my goals I have made some sacrifices. The areas here and here have already been sold off, they'll be developed into exclusive time-share holiday properties with a small high quality estate of cottages. I too am carrying out building work, various redundant barns are being converted for holiday lets. This will create a certain amount of local work. I intend using local craftsmen, labourers and the work will be spread over the next two years. Our aim at this stage is to turn it into a profit-making concern. I have been looking into the various enterprises that operate off Home Farm land. I have taken advice from various organisations and drawn my own conclusions.

'The fish & game farm, leased and run by Alan Turner . . .' Turner sat up and took special interest, smiling and nodding to anyone who might be interested in who Turner might be. No-one was. 'At present,' Tate continued, 'it supplies fish to local restaurants, a few birds for its own shoots and some to other shoots in the region. These activities will be expanded and the fish farm will be open to the public. It can be an outing for all the family, Mum and Dad can come up to choose their fish and the children can buy bags of feed to throw into the tanks. The increased volume of traffic will require an access road to be built and greater parking facilities. The game side of the operation will also expand. I intend to increase the number of shooting days dramatically, so the emphasis of bird production will be on supplying our own shoots. Furthermore a clay pigeon shoot will be set up. This will be a completely separate enterprise and will in no way affect the birds from a noise level point of view. The site I have chosen is well away from the woodland and will not affect the noise level or any other plans.

'The Feldmann farm will become a Museum of Rural Life with an emphasis on rare animal breeds and a collection of antique agricultural equipment, a study centre for schools and colleges will be included in the expansion – obviously this is a long-

term plan.

'I acquired the estate with the intention of maintaining as much of the natural flora and fauna as possible but I'm a businessman and within my self-imposed brief to make it pay, this area here will be turned into a championship standard golf course. By the year 2000 what was once a remote corner of the country with a dwindling population heavily dependent on an unviable farming industry relying more and more on subsidies will have been transformed into a major tourist area, holiday makers' paradise, designed to compete with anything to be found in this country or abroad. It will sport the kind of facilities this part of the world has only dreamed about so far, a high class touring caravan site with clubhouses and shops.

'Quality and comfort will be the watchwords, catering for the entertainment needs of the whole family. It will become the major attraction in the North of England, revitalising the whole region and meeting the leisure needs of a million or more visitors.'

Frank Tate had every reason to believe that the time was right to replace Beckindale's agricultural base with tourism. Six years later even Jack and Sarah would be converting a barn as a self-catering venue for tourists, although Jack would never stop pushing his dream, talking at the same time to his wife about launching a co-operative effort, a farm shop to market all the local organic lamb and beef.

NY's agribusiness had failed, and Frank was shrewd enough to realise that the huge industrial and market changes which had recommended NY to its purpose, had, at the same time, thrown up a nostalgic desire for what had been. The idyll of Old Rural England had made for emotive and nostalgic literature, poems and art, since the turn of the cen-

Frank Tate's holiday village opened its doors for the first time in the summer of 1992.

tury, and the same idyll lay somewhere deep in the fabric of the Union Jack which had waved millions to heroic deaths in two world wars. But by the late 1960s and early '70s, when the mad rat race of urban living had really got underway, a sense of what had been lost had translated into a desire to visit or even own a piece of the countryside, ownership being the way most people expressed their desire for a thing by then.

In 1977, Sam Pearson hadn't been able to believe the price which the Estate Agent from Hotten had put on Hawthorn Cottage when Joe had put it up for sale following the break-up of his marriage to Christine Sharp – £16,000 against less than £200 which he well recalled Jameson paying for it.

A year or so later, at about the time the Verneys sold up, Matt had commented on the steady increase in 'stoney-faced' holidaymakers and people coming from the towns and cities with an eye to purchasing property in the area, and Joe had complained, 'They're looking at the land as an investment.'

Some townies had tried to escape the rat-race altogether, and came to the Dales failing utterly to see that it took more than a sense of romance to make such a move work.

When Ray and Sarah Oswell turned up from London to live in a cottage on the edge of Emmerdale in the 1970s, with a plan for self-sufficient living, they demonstrated a naive lack of understanding of what had happened to rural culture over 100 years. Self-sufficient living on a smallholding was long since a dream. When a storm brought down a tree on top of their cottage, it was as if Nature herself was educating them. They returned to London, but the Sugdens weren't laughing. The Oswells had made them see again what the long-term resident of Beckindale could too easily take for granted – that a workable relationship with the spirit of such a place was not to be traded for anything.

A century after the Industrial Revolution sounded the death-knell of English rural culture, Frank Tate's ultimatum to the people of Beckindale was to Disneyfy their culture or watch it die. What Frank planned was anything but idyllic, but it was a workable strategy because that was what people now wanted. What matter if the tourists would only get the sentimental gloss? As Frank said to Joe, 'Farmers were only romantics anyway.'

This then was the broad outline of the pattern which Henry had seen emerging all those years before, when NY Estates had started pouring chemicals on the land and Estates manager Trevor Thatcher had threatened the traditional way of Nellie Ratcliffe's life with a self-interested strategy backed by the law.

Self-interest had been the keynote, profit the motive. It had upset the whole balance of life in the

Holiday cottages in Frank Tate's complex – 'By the year 2000,' he boasted, 'what was once a remote corner of the country with a dwindling population dependent on an unviable farming industry relying more and more on subsidies will have been transformed into a major tourist area.'

The view from Hawthorn Cottage, which was said to be worth £5,000 alone twenty years earlier.

Dales. But had there been any realistic alternative? The economic sense of the scientific revolution may have been put into question when NY Estates pulled out, but as Joe said, the future is with us, there could be no going back.

In Beckindale, Agribusiness would simply give way to Tourism and, in other areas, what the National Union of Farmers refer to as the 'Yuppiefication effect', where outsiders with very different attitudes make farmers feel they no longer belong to the communities in which they live.

There would be no return to the old culture. Farming was now a business, and statistics from the Samaritans bear terrible testament to the pressures

By 1996 even Jack and his wife, Sarah (pictured here), would be converting a barn at Hawthorn into a self-catering venue for tourists.

Sandie Merrick with married builder Phil Pearce.

on the small independent today. The deaths of 983 farmers and farm workers between 1979 and 1990 are registered as suicides, and suicide is now the second most common cause of death in farmers up to 45.

Evidence of the consequences of social change which had occurred in Beckindale in the same period was, by the 1990s, becoming equally clear in statistics of the number of children born to unmarried or divorced parents – children who often seemed to be drawn to one another, as if bent on replicating the pattern.

Sandie Merrick, daughter of divorcees Tom and Pat Merrick, had conceived a baby, Louise, with Andy Longthorn and had her adopted. She had then returned to Beckindale and fallen in love with married builder Phil Pearce.

Jackie Merrick, conceived out of wedlock by Jack and Pat, had married Kathy Bates, daughter of divorcees Caroline and Malcolm Bates, after Jackie had pulled himself out of the despondency and heartache over Tom and Pat's divorce.

In 1991, two years after Jackie's death in a shooting accident, Kathy would marry Chris Tate. Three years later, during which Chris's father, Frank, became involved in a bitter divorce from his stepmother, Kim, Chris had an adulterous affair with Rachel Hughes, and he and Kathy were divorced.

Rachel, whom Kathy would accuse of making a career out of adultery, was herself the daughter of divorcees David and Kate Hughes. In 1990 Rachel had had an affair with married man Pete Whiteley, and then become engaged to Michael Feldmann, son of single mother Elizabeth Feldmann.

Fifteen years or so after the live-in affair of Kathy Gimbel and Joe Sugden had so outraged Beckindale, the divorce rate had soared, but the effect on the children was only now being assessed.

When Jack had returned to Beckindale in 1980 and married Pat Merrick, Jackie's hostility towards him for coming between his mother and father eventually drove Jack to tell Jackie that he and not Tom was his real father. It nearly destroyed the boy, and Annie had been furious with Jack for being so insensitive. 'The man who brought Jackie up and played with him and put bandages on his cut knee is his father, Jack,' she said. 'Where were you when he was growing up? What claims have you on his affections? You've hurt that boy by telling him something he never need have known . . . Tom Merrick is his real father.'

Annie always manned the ramparts when family was under fire. Family was the last bastion of all she held dear. She could never allow children to suffer. But that was because she shared her father Sam's view that family was the circle in the pond next to God. Blood had nothing to do with it. It was all about love, selfless love.

When Joe Sugden started dating divorcee Kate Hughes (they married in 1989), Kate's young son Mark by her first husband came upon them together and was so distraught he ran away from home. Annie was deeply upset that Joe had been so self-interested that he had given no consideration to how the young minds of Kate's children might respond to the affair.

Jackie, who had already lived through exactly the same scene, described his feelings to his wife, Kathy: 'A few years ago it was me going through what this young un's going through now. I just couldn't understand how my mum could move in with another man.'

'But you didn't run away,' Kathy said.

'Oh no, I stayed to fight. But I felt just like he does, so what right have I got to tell him to go back to his mother and live with Joe at Emmerdale.'

In the end, young Mark made it all the way to Hull,

Pete Whiteley's father Bill tends to his son's injuries after David Hughes had attacked him for having an adulterous affair with his daughter, Rachel.

where he planned to take a boat to find his father, who was stationed in Germany. For Annie, this was the final straw. Five years after Sam's death the ripples in the pond had finally disappeared, and for her at least there was nothing, an emotional vacuum.

To begin with the signs that something was up were small, but then one day everyone became very concerned. Annie returned from shopping but couldn't find the tea. She was sure she'd bought it, so why wasn't it there? 'Somebody must have taken it,' she said to Matt. Matt looked at her and then Kathy, rather quizzically. Kathy suggested maybe it was still in the car. Matt said he couldn't see what all the fuss was about.

'But I know that I bought it.'

'It'll turn up,' Matt reassured her, 'Meanwhile t'farm is not going to grind to a halt if we drink coffee is it?'

'You all think I'm being old and silly.'

Matt knew better: 'I know you're worried about Joe and Mark. Why don't you give Dolly a call, get her to come over for a chat.'

'Why do you think she'll know where I put the tea?'

Later Kathy told Jackie to talk to her, and Jackie agreed, 'OK, where is she?'

'Sitting in the parlour looking at last night's

Above, Kate and Joe. Left, Mark and sister Rachel in 1988.

dishes.'

'Kathy says you're not feeling very well,' he began when he found Annie.

'I'm tired, lad, old and tired.'

'What's the matter? What's wrong?'

'I wish I knew.'

'Are you worrying about Mark?'

Annie frowned at this, 'I know I ought to be.'

'I don't understand.'

'I'm not myself lad, that's all,' and then she smiled.

'What about these pills, Ma?' he said. Annie looked at him, confused, and Jackie continued: 'I don't like to see me old grandma like this.'

'Not me is it?'

'No.' Annie,

'No,' she hesitated for a moment, and then shrugged. 'Tranquilisers. What a word. Can't say I feel much of that these days. Can't say I feel much of anything.'

It was 9 o'clock in the evening when Matt came through from the outhouse to find the kitchen in darkness, Annie sitting in her dressing gown, her hair in a mess.

'Are you alright?' he asked.

Annie nodded.

'What are you doing?'

'Having a sit-down.'

'Can I get you owt? Summat to eat?'

She shook her head.

'They're all getting at me Matt.'

'They're worried about you, Annie.'

'They're telling me that I don't need my pills, but I do.'

'Shall I call the doctor?'

'What for? I've got my pills.'

Later Henry arrived and told Annie she must stop taking the anti-depressants she had been prescribed. Annie said, 'Don't you start on me, Henry. Jack's already been nagging. I mean Matt. He said I was taking too many, but I've only taken them when I've needed them, y'know, when . . . I needed them. I've not had one today.'

'Matt said you had.'

Annie, no longer pitiful, came on suddenly hard: 'What does he know? He's not been with me all day. I've had Dolly getting at me . . . and Kathy, and Matt spying on me. I'm not going to have it, not in my own home. Now, are you going to get them for me or am I going to have to get up and get them for myself?'

Henry tried everything that night. He began by telling her how he had always admired her strength. 'You've fought to keep your family going. You've been their strength.' But she shook her head, 'I've lived too long for other people. Jacob had it

Kathy Merrick confronts Annie about her use of tranquilisers.

right. He lived for himself, did my Jacob. He didn't give a damn about anybody.'

'Your husband was a weak man,' Henry said. 'He couldn't cope with things. You can . . . or you could. Joe and his new family, they'll need the old Annie Sugden just as much as before. Mebbe Jack and Marian too, and me.'

'But where are they when I need them? The only time any of you talk to me is to take fault.'

'No-one dare talk to you because every time it turns into a row . . . If you give up now then all anyone will remember of Annie Sugden is that she was a quitter. They won't remember the strong wonderful woman who's really Annie. Not this way, we're going to get you off these pills now. Where are they?'

'I'm not telling you. Go home.'

'Where are they?'

'You came in here throwing your weight around when you first came to Beckindale. It didn't work then either. Other folk might think of you as kind, clever Henry Wilks. I know you better. You're nowt but an old fool who once asked me to marry him. Stop interfering.'

Henry saw some hope in this and replied sardonically, 'Nice to know that some of the old Annie Sugden's there any road. They haven't destroyed the nasty bits.'

Then he walked over to the mantlepiece and looked at a picture of Jack and his second son by Pat, Robert. He looked at it for a moment and then noticed the panic on Annie's face. The tablets were behind it. He grabbed the bottle and headed for the Aga.

Annie, seeing what he was up to, pleaded, almost in tears: 'I'm sorry, Henry, give me 'em, please?'

'They're going where they should've gone weeks ago.'

'Please!'

Henry opened the Aga door, paused for a split second and then threw them in.

At the same moment, unknown to them, Joe and Kate were picking up Mark at Hull docks. Henry sat with her in silence, but as the night wore on she became increasingly agitated as the worry at not having her pills intensified. Actual physical withdrawal would take place in another twenty-four hours. But through this night the stress would take its terrible toll.

Henry suggested she went to bed.

Annie spoke very softly, 'You don't understand, Henry, I'm scared . . .You threw them away, it was a wicked thing to do.'

It was as if Annie was suffering all the heartache, all the disappointment of the years heaped up in one dose. What was it she had said back in 1974 when Joe was suffering his own agonies over the break-up of his marriage to Christine?

'Ah, lad, lad, thou'st had a blow. I wish I could have taken it for thee.'

But Annie had taken it. She had taken all the blows for her family and friends in Beckindale over the years, soaked them up like a sponge, which was now full to overflowing. 'Sometimes,' Joe had commented in 1975, 'I wonder if there's anything or anyone that Ma won't take the responsibility for . . .'

At 3.30am, Annie said simply, 'I just want to die, Henry. I think I will.'

When Henry tried to reach her, she reacted with terrible hostility – 'Don't touch me. I don't want anyone to touch me.' – and Henry pulled away, shocked. It is was if, for a split second, he'd seen the demon inside.

He moved to the telephone to call the hospital. 'No Henry don't let them take me away I want to stay here. I won't shout at you again, I promise.'

Unsure of what was happening he returned the phone to its cradle.

At 6.30am they were still there and Annie's symptoms were more physical – 'I'm sweating, my heart's pumping . . . I can't breathe Henry.'

Henry went for the phone again and dialled the doctor.

When at 7.30 the doctor came down from upstairs he found Henry, Matt and Jackie waiting, and he was very annoyed that the pills had been thrown away. He told them to contact the surgery and request a list of organisations to help her get off them, 'if that is what she really wants.'

Tranquilisers are no longer prescribed so freely. In Annie's case they proved hopelessly inadequate as a panacea for a problem which had its roots in the huge changes which had occurred over twenty years.

As fertilisers to the soil, where overuse leads to structural breakdown, all that the tranquilisers did for Annie was to rub love out.

A New Beginning?

The passenger plane crash which devastated Beckindale on the evening of December 30, 1993, was a disaster of Biblical proportions – not even the name of the village survived. Besides those of the villagers killed, there were 250 airline passengers and crew said to have been seen falling from the sky like rain. Laid out in the school hall for identification, the bodies included that of Mark Hughes, found clutching the remains of a vacuum cleaner. His stepfather Joe Sugden's order to return it had taken him into the very path of disaster.

The churchyard of St Mary's. On the first day of January, 1994, the village of Beckindale had to cope with more dead than in all the time most of its inhabitants had lived there.

Eric Pollard roamed the death fields of Beckindale like some survivor of nuclear holocaust, crying for his wife, Elizabeth. Why Eric should survive and not Elizabeth seemed to speak volumes about the indiscriminate nature of fate, and Elizabeth's son, Michael, did not find it easy to accept that his stepfather's grief was genuine, given that her passing effectively freed Eric from the strong arm of the law.

Elizabeth Feldmann, as she was called before Pollard married her in 1992, had struggled to earn a living from Blackthorn Farm, part of the Home Farm Estate, for twenty-seven years. In 1990 she had decided to call it a day and asked Alan Turner

The body of Mark Hughes still clutching the vacuum cleaner,
which his stepfather, Joe, had insisted he return.

for a job at the fish and game farm. Subsequently, she had become close to Alan and joined him at the Woolpack after he'd taken it over in 1991. She had also agreed to allow Eric Pollard to organise the dispersal sale at Blackthorn.

There'd been some jealousy over Alan's close friendship with Caroline Bates, and again (this time from Alan) when on one occasion Elizabeth had got drunk with Eric. Then Elizabeth had seen Eric again, and later he won her over in typical style. He returned to Elizabeth a painting worth £1,000, which he had sneakily arranged to purchase for himself at the Blackthorn sale for far less than it was worth.

One step back; two steps forward. It was typical of Pollard's tactics, if only Elizabeth had realised. When he had married her the following year, it emerged that he had never been divorced from his first wife, and the final straw was drawn by Pollard when he had stolen cheques from Frank Tate's cheque book, which Frank had given Elizabeth for safe keeping.

However heroic in classical myth, the workings of

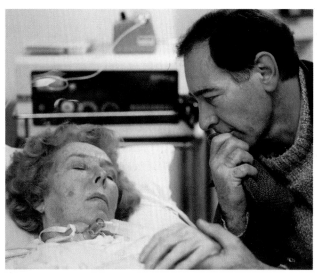

Jack with his mother, Annie, unconscious in hospital.

Dr McAllister, his wife, Angharad, and children, Luke and Jessica, emerge from their home to the devastation.

Skipdale Bridge, where Frank and Jack combined forces to solve the problem of access for relief workers.

fate can seem bereft of logic when their destructive force favours such negative elements as Eric Pollard. There were many on that black day who questioned the morality and fairness of their tragic loss, and no vicar in the village to reassure them. For by this time Beckindale was a team ministry with the right to consult a spiritual adviser restricted to one week in three.

On Kathy Tate, fate had played a quirkier trick. Led by the stallion, Samson, to a pile of rubble outside the Woolpack, Kathy's boyfriend, Josh, heard a pathetically faint cry for help. Moving away some surface debris, Josh saw that it was Chris Tate, the husband of the woman he had been about to run away with. There was good reason for Josh to feel more trapped than Chris, for in spite of the mound of rubble which took three men with Samson's help hours to dismantle, Josh knew in his heart that Chris was badly hurt. With Kathy holding her husband's hand and reassuring him, what space was there left for him to move?

Chris was paralysed and would be consigned to a wheelchair. Kathy cradled his head in her arms in a mixture of pain and emotion, and Chris turned on the agony for the two lovers: 'Stupid isn't it . . . Something like this puts it all in perspective . . . You can make all the plans in the world and then . . .'

The impact of the disaster gave everyone cause to re-think. Seth was missing, presumed dead, his house reduced to rubble. Alan Turner was devastated that they had parted on such angry terms. Close to tears he admitted he couldn't imagine the Woolpack without the old eccentric at the bar.

In the wreck of his car, Joe crawled over the body of Leonard Kempinski, his gaping eyes blind to this world, and began babbling urgently to Annie's deathly silent form, 'Oh Ma, be all right. Please God be all right.' A few miles away, a couple of men passed from body to body, looting. Before too long the roads would be jammed with sightseers who had heard of the tragedy on the news.

But fate has a way of finding the best in us too. Turner's new assistant at the Woolpack, Shirley Foster, set up a relief kitchen with Kim. Alan had met Shirley, an ex-prostitute, at a drop-in centre in Leeds, they would marry a month or so after the crash. The village doctor, Bernard McAllister, and his wife, Angharad, newly arrived in Beckindale, also worked tirelessly for the shocked survivors. And Frank Tate and Jack Sugden combined forces to solve the problem of access for relief workers over Skipdale bridge, caused by work on the water main.

With Kim's stables burned out and most of her horses dead, Frank took his ex-wife home and finally gave her the prettily wrapped present from his car. It was a bronze figure. 'I . . .er . . .thought it looked like Dark Star,' Frank stuttered, both of them aware that it was all there was left to remind Kim of her favourite horse. 'Oh, it does . . .' Kim started, 'Oh Frank, it's beautiful.'

Then Seth ambled innocently in to the Woolpack and received a drink on the house from an overjoyed landlord: 'Least I could do after what happened the other night. I hope you'll take it as an apology.' Seth, who had been safely tucked up in bed in Filey with Betty Eagleton throughout the disaster, accepted the olive branch and drank with relish at Turner's unprecedented generosity, before enquiring, 'How much *did* you raise towards my operation?'

Events, it seemed, had come full circle.

Among those who did not die, but for whom nevertheless it spelled an end, was Annie Sugden. Lying unconscious in hospital she would never return in quite the same way again, preferring retirement in Spain even without her husband, Leonard, who had succumbed in the crash.

As for Joe, his passion for farming was spent – he had worked for a while in 1992 at Frank's holiday village – and never recovered his position at Emmerdale. The following year he would be sitting, his leg in plaster on a seat in front of him, in the kitchen at Hawthorn Cottage, giving Jack a piece of his mind about the disintegrating fortunes of the Sugden family.

To Joe's way of thinking, they'd been 'stumbling from one crisis to another. I'm just sick to death of coming second best all the time,' Joe said, and concluded, 'This family is cursed.' But to Jack, Joe

Sadly the happiness of Shirley Foster and Alan Turner was short lived. Following their marriage in 1994, Shirley was killed during an armed raid on Emmerdale's Post Office, when she and post mistress Viv Windsor were taken hostage.

sounded for all the world like their feckless father, Jacob, a quarter of a century earlier. The problem, as Jack saw it, was that Joe had been running a race with no purpose beyond the race itself. He had lost his purpose from the moment he attached his colours to NY Estates.

Jack, with enough else to contend with at this point in 1994 – his little daughter, Victoria, was in hospital with a life threatening condition and his wife, Sarah, was away with her – refused to be drawn into his brother's depression. Joe had been feeling sorry for himself for too long, and as far as Jack was concerned this busted ankle of his was just a good excuse to continue sitting around and whingeing when he could be pulling his weight around the farm.

'I'm trying to run a farm,' Jack said to him, 'trying to make a living and keep a business going. My wife's away and my baby could be dying, and all you can do is sit around and talk about the curse of the bloody Sugdens.'

What a turn round from the days when it was Jack who skitted here, there and everywhere, following his muse, rather than knuckling down to work on the farm. But at least Jack had never compromised it.

There were already five generations of Sugdens in St Mary's. Now Joe's part in the Sugden story was about to fold.

'You know who the curse is, Joe?' he shouted at his brother, 'You are! You are the curse!'

Not waiting for the dust to settle, Jack shuffled various tenants around in Sugden property and left Joe without a place to live. Then, after calling Annie in Spain, he gave it to his brother straight.

'I've spoken to Ma,' he said simply.

'How is she?' enquired Joe.

'I've told her to expect a visitor.'

'Who?'

'You.'

And that, both brothers knew, was the end for Joe in Emmerdale. Sadly, it spelled the end for Joe altogether, for he was killed shortly afterwards in a car crash in Spain.

For the Sugdens, the tragedy spelled the culmination of an era. Only Jack remained. But the past would never be forgotten, for henceforth the village of Beckindale would have a new name – Emmerdale – the name of the Sugdens' farm, a constant reminder of the days when Annie Sugden held sway and farming was still the economic mainstay and cultural fulcrum on which life turned.

Frank and Kim, who seemed all set to take Emmerdale into the future, celebrated their re-union in marriage for the second time, nearly a year after the disaster, in Ripon Cathedral. It looked to be the perfect new beginning after a period of terrible emotional turmoil, which had begun in 1992 when Kim had fallen from her horse at the Hotten Show, broken her leg and lost their baby, an event which had led inexorably to divorce.

Their first marriage in March, 1986, had followed the death of Frank's first wife from cancer of the liver, Frank himself easing her out of her final agony, as he admitted publicly at the Hunt Ball in 1990. Kim had been Frank's secretary.

Frank Tate was a shrewd and complex man, but he was also an alcoholic. Kim was a beautiful woman and just as complex. When they arrived in Beckindale in 1989, Kim's real interest, other than Frank, lay not in his plans for tourism so much as in horses. That's not to say that she didn't support her husband in his endeavours. In 1991, when the holiday village opened, she was not averse to lending her obvious physical attractions and powerful personality to its launch, even appearing in the brochure, and in the same year she gave Frank £35,000 from the sale of one

Frank and Kim were married again in Ripon Cathedral on December 22nd, 1994, their reunion suggesting renewed stability at Home Farm, the economic hub of the village.

of her horses to pay his tax bill.

In pursuit of her aim to set up commercial stables at Home Farm (where she would employ Kathy Bates as stablehand), Kim made it her business to get well in with the Demdale Hunt, agreeing that it could use Home Farm land. Unfortunately, she hadn't cleared this with Frank first, and when she and Dolly (by then employed as housekeeper at Home Farm) prepared the stirrup cup for the Boxing Day meet in 1990, on a tressle table on the veranda of the Hall, Frank, who was drying out at the time, tipped it over the ground, saying, 'I thought we'd made a pact. No alcohol until after the New Year . . . It's bad enough having the hunt here without all of you getting boozed up beforehand.'

Joe had been there and, rather embarrassed for Kim, took her part – 'It's a tradition, Frank,' he

said, 'The hunt always starts with the stirrup cup.'

'Tradition!' Frank exploded, 'It's just an excuse to get tanked up before riding like drunken yobbos and causing God knows that sort of mayhem. Well, I'm not having it! Dolly, make some tea and coffee, will you?'

The hunt is a tradition much abused and came under fire by others in Emmerdale at this time. Rachel Hughes was against it on the basis of its cruelty to foxes. Again, it was Joe who took her up on it. 'Foxes are vermin Rachel. Foxes'll kill all the hens in a hen run just for the hell of it.'

But Rachel wouldn't have it: 'That's not true. Foxes live mostly on rabbits and wild birds and rats and mice. They reckon only 5% ever eats poultry.'

'Oh aye,' said Joe, 'Who's they? Some towny do-gooder, I suppose?'

'The British Field Sports Society actually,' Rachel corrected him.

'Ah, well, it's a great British tradition and you hardly ever catch the foxes anyway.'

Kim made it her business to get well in with the Demdale Hunt.

Saboteur Jessica McAllister was knocked unconscious by the hunt master's horse.

'Why do it then?' she asked.

Rachel might have tackled Joe on the practice of covering foxes' lairs so that they have no escape. But Rachel is something of an idealist and doesn't always think things through. In 1994, she became a hunt saboteur, encouraging Jessica McAllister to join her. As the hunt master's horse galloped towards them, Jessica leapt forward and came between his horse and the hedge it was about to jump. Jessica was knocked unconscious and McAllister sacked Rachel from her position as his receptionist as a result.

In his day, Amos had seen the hunt as a colourful page out of Horse and Hound: 'The grandest spectacle of country life, a pack of fine foxhounds, everyone in hunting pink, well-groomed thoroughbreds thirsting to be off, a blast on the horn and away on the trail of wily Reynard.'

'I don't suppose this enthusiasm is anything to do with the amount of trade they bring?' Henry had commented drily.

'The mercenary aspect of it had never crossed my mind,' Amos had insisted, looking at his old partner down his own ample nose.

Zoe, soon to be Emmerdale's vet, was unsure about her view on the matter: 'I'm on Rachel's side. The hunt's just a rampage across the country, terrifying a poor little animal, whose only crime is to want to feed its family. On the other hand I suppose hunting doesn't seem as important as some other things I see in my job, so-called pets being starved to death, battery farming, that's what really upsets me.'

It was an interesting distinction between hunting and exploitation. If hunting is cruel exploitation, its long tradition doesn't make it any better. Most huntsmen would grant that it is an ineffective means of vermin control, but have difficulty in justifying their behaviour to Rachel.

But even when man hunted his quarry for food, there was an additional attraction. The hunt satisfied man's predatory instincts, just as a deal satisfied Frank Tate's. It is odd that Frank so despised the hunt, because he had the hunter's instinct for the kill. Perhaps the hunt was too much a mirror to the truth about him.

What has changed is not man, but the context in which he lives. However much Rachel might wish for a ban, men will always find themselves a forum to

Kim Tate and Kathy Bates ride out from Home Farm three years before the tragedy.

sharpen their claws and exercise them, as indeed will women, as will shortly be seen.

Kim was publicly humiliated and furious with her husband when he upset the stirrup cup, but way down in the pit of his alcohol dependency, all that Frank could see was that she'd let him down, 'I thought you wanted to help me,' he whined.

Frank's drinking got so bad, that that same year he even missed Zoe's graduation day, holed up in some hotel room with a hangover. Kim realised something had to be done. What Frank and indeed their relationship needed, she decided, was something to bind them closer together, which was when she started talking to him about having a baby – not a simple solution, for Frank had had a vasectomy. But Kim was rarely to be denied. When Frank agreed to have the operation reversed, Kim poured all his booze away by way of celebration.

How far, subconsciously, the loss of Kim's baby in 1992 influenced future events in Kim's life one cannot be sure, but it hit Frank badly and time and again the baby would be held up as a symbol of something which had eluded them.

The loss spelled a speedy return to the bad times – Frank hit the bottle, Kim had an affair with Neil Kincaid, Frank slashed all her clothes and threatened

Kim's fall at the Hotten Show, 1992, when she miscarried, an event which led inexorably to her first split from Frank.

wife Sarah.

'But they arrive at every disaster . . .,' she had replied.

'That's my point – I think they encourage people to be traumatised.'

'Of course they do – they don't want people bottling it up for years and ruining their lives.'

'I'm not saying people like Joe aren't suffering from stress – he was in it, he was there – but look at all those kids, they weren't in the stables, they didn't see the horses die . . .'

'No, they just heard them screaming . . . How's Robert going to react when he hears about his gran, who he loves more than you and me put together?'

'Ma's not dead. We'll keep a close eye on Robert, make sure he's alright.'

'Ever heard the phrase "in denial", Jack?'

'Yeah – it's therapist mumbo-jumbo for not facing up to things – and you're still wrong.'

Kim Tate's affair with Neil Kincaid followed the loss of her baby and led to violence and a bitter divorce.

to kill Kincaid with a shotgun, and finally she and Frank became involved in a bitter divorce. Then, in the summer of 1993, when the divorce was proceeding, Frank's son, Chris, a pale image of the father, who held Kim responsible for getting his father back on the booze, showed his rather tarnished metal by snapping up Kim's shares and using his new voting power to call an Emergency General Meeting at which he tried to dislodge Frank from the chairmanship of Tate Holdings.

Now, in 1994, the plane crash had cauterised all these old wounds and seemingly brought the family back together.

The feeling of a community pulling together after the tragedy was a source of real optimism for Emmerdale's future. In Sam Pearson's day, such a response would have been taken as read, but after the crash the Emmerdale community was put to the test in the modern context and was not found wanting.

Jack's adverse reaction to the team of outsider social workers and therapists who had butted in with their psycho-speak was a compliment to the quality of support which the community had given spontaneously to both survivors and bereaved.

'There's a whole sort of . . . "stress management industry" sprung up in Beckindale – social workers, therapists, everyone . . .,' he had complained to his

Amidst devastation and heartbreak there were rays of hope, like the rescue of Nick Bates's daughter, Alice, shown here.

Jack's point was that you don't need dozens of social workers knocking at your door after a tragedy like this. Victims of the Marchioness disaster four years earlier had also complained of being 'pestered' by volunteers. The emergence of the 'stress management industry' was a second rate answer to the collapse of the network of family and community which used to come to people's aid.

So the tragedy brought out the best in Emmerdale.

But would the new spirit last? Would the crash open people's eyes to the traditional purpose of a community like Emmerdale? Would it bind people together as once before?

It was certainly true that even before the disaster, the village maintained something of its closeness,

completeness and separateness from the outside world, as one particular incomer found out.

When Cockney wide-boy Vic Windsor came to Beckindale with his wife Viv and young family to take over the corner shop and Post Office shortly before the disaster in 1993, they came, as Viv would say three years later, 'to be part of a community, a place where people help each other out.'

But they shouldn't have been surprised at the reaction of Beckindalers to foreigners from down South taking over one of the main focal points of village life. It is a mark of a close-weave culture providing the kind of community spirit which they wanted that it doesn't throw its doors open to out-siders. In any case, to begin with the Windsors did little to recommend themselves.

Cockney and Dalesman cultures are as indelible as one another, if not as deep rooted in time. One big difference is marked by accent of course, but another, as Vic's introduction to the Woolpack showed, by humour and pace and that Cockney familiarity – too presumptive for the Dalesman's taste, especially when casually barbed.

Beckindale seemed stuck in a time warp to Vic. But there was more than a suspicion that Vic himself

Cockneys Vic and Viv Windsor survey the map which led them to Beckindale with Vic's daughter, Kelly, and Viv's son, Scott, in search of a community where, in Viv's words, 'people help each other out.'

The village Post Office, where the Windsors now hold sway.

Unlike Kim on Dark Star, Joe was not amused when he rose from the mud after Vic Windsor's Ford zapped by.

was not sold on the present. There was his car for a start – a classic Ford Zodiac, and his penchant for '60s oldies – was it *Livin' Doll* he was singing as the saloon swung into view? To anyone listening, all they would have heard was the roar of the Ford engine as it careered far too fast round the country roads.

Vic's was the clichéd townie's entrance trick. Failing to see Kim exercising Dark Star, Vic zapped past, and the horse backed up alarmingly. Kim shouted, 'Slow down!' but Vic was already gone. 'Stand! Stand!' she said sternly to the stallion and Joe tried to take him by the noseband. But it was no good – 'Get out of the way, Joe,' she screamed as the horse barged past him through the open gate, leaving Joe face down on the ground.

So to the Woolpack, where Vic settled wife, Viv, and

children, Kelly and Scott, at an outside table while he ventured in to order some food.

There'd been a buzz of excitement in the family all day. Vic hadn't told them about the Post Office or that he had arranged to pick up the keys at the pub. The Windsors had been scouring Cornwall and Devon for weeks for a place to de-bunk to, but found nothing they liked. Vic had a feeling about the North and as he bounced into the bar, his energy was running high. But he was met by . . . nothing.

The bar was such a void he nearly missed his step. There was no-one even to serve him, only Seth eyeballing him at the bar.

Vic acknowledged him with an 'All right?'

Seth lifted the lid on Beckindale a whisker with a 'How do,' and then slammed it tight shut.

The quiet was almost deafening. It was as if time itself stood still, like one of those Western ghost towns where rounds of tumbleweed scud about a dusty waste. Vic's eyes roamed over the place – there was nothing else to do – and inevitably they settled on Seth once more.

'No news of Glenn Miller then?'

Seth just stared, as if Vic were from another world.

Then Carol, Turner's assistant, emerged at last from the back room and apologised for keeping him. 'What can I get you?' she asked.

'S'all right sweetheart,' Vic gave her, warming up again. 'Two cokes, half a lager shandy and a pint of your best bitter. Oh, and a bar snack menu when you've done the other drinks.'

But of course the Woolpack didn't do a bar snack menu. 'There's a wine bar next door,' she told him, 'if you fancy something to eat.'

Vic was astonished, but less so than he sounded: 'Wine bar? Well, wonders never cease.'

'Yes, well, the 20th century hasn't exactly passed us by,' Carol replied. 'Most of us are aware of what's going on in the world. Surprising though it may seem to you.'

Carol hadn't been slow to pick up Vic's theme or the way he was milking it, but her response was no challenge for the Eastender: 'It's amazing what you can pick up, isn't it – huddled round your wireless sets of an evening.'

Vic hadn't actually said anything rude. It was just

his breezy, familiar, cocky, Cockney way. But it was not Carol's or Beckindale's. You'd be hard put to find anyone more obscure to a Dalesman than a cocksure Cockney bent on taking the piss.

Seth, who had been all this time wavering on a knife edge between understanding Vic and falling headlong into the morass to which Vic had led him, jumped the wrong way.

'Here, Glenn Miller,' he began slowly. 'He were that bloke in wartime with band, weren't he?'

Vic exploded with laughter and Seth crept back inside himself, outraged, just as Joe walked in and demanded to know whether Vic was the driver of the Zodiac parked outside.

'Haven't you heard of the Country Code?' he shouted. 'This is the countryside not a London race track . . .' and so on.

Vic, who hadn't even seen Dark Star, was at a complete loss to know what it was all about,

'This some kind of pub quiz or what?' he ventured, which only served to wind up Joe further.

Turner, who had by this time appeared, was roused to intervene and, to give him his due, he saw Joe to the door before turning to Vic – 'This is a respectable establishment,' he said to the incomer, 'We don't have, nor do we want, any trouble.'

Flabbergasted at his reception, Vic left Turner and Seth yet more aghast with his next remark – 'Turn it in. I only came in here to have a drink and pick up some keys . . .'

Of course the Woolpack, now that Turner was ensconced, was a good deal more like home for a Cockney wide-boy than in Amos's day, even if Vic couldn't credit it at first. Besides the new look and restaurant fare in the old tap room, there was the regular presence of Eric Pollard, who might have been quite at home in a number of pubs in the East End of London.

Having recovered his composure after the loss of Elizabeth, Eric had become engaged in 1994 in one of his most ambitious scams. Dressed as a fireman, he and his gang had caused a diversion at a nearby stately home, Briardale Hall, and successfully looted it of £150,000 worth of goods. He had used Turner as his alibi, taking him to his home so drunk that he passed out and remained unconcscious until Pollard had returned from the robbery.

Pollard's latching on to Turner did very nearly lose Turner the Woolpack. Pollard knew that he was still not out of the financial problems which attended his takeover of the pub, and was keen to push him into an ever more vulnerable position, lending Turner £500 on one occasion to bet at the races and keeping a careful note of other sums he had leant him too.

The crunch came when Turner ran into problems with the VAT man and Pollard offered to go through his books. He turned up enough to frighten Turner into nearly accepting a loan of £20,000 to sort them out, with the Woolpack as security. Fortunately for Turner, Carloine Bates stepped in and, despite Pollard's efforts to put her off the scent, discovered what he was up to.

For once the conman got what he deserved, a knee in the groin and a ban from the pub.

Now, Pollard was about to entice into Emmerdale a family which would have more of an impact on the village even than him. With some of his newfound wealth, Pollard decided to go into the party promotion business.

He had bought a field on the corner of Connelton Road and Blackmill Lane, and generously designated it as the site for a 'rave'. No-one over the age of twenty-five in Emmerdale had the least idea what to expect. Even Vic Windsor from the vice capital showed his naivety to his stepson Scott over the intended agenda, and settled in the end for all that he needed to know.

Drugs apart, if there were going to be a lot of manically dancing, hot sweaty bodies, they'd be in need of refreshment. So Vic stocked up the boot of his car with soft drinks from the village store and set himself up on Pollard's site.

Word of the 'rave' spread far and wide, as did the music, and the village was inundated with vehicles and kids from outside, all bent on a good time.

There was a charge at the gate, picked up by young Luke McAllister, who had gone down well with the girls of the village since he arrived the year before. Luke's long, rather studiously dischevelled, blond hair, hunky torso and dreamily simmering eyes all combined to suggest to his female admirers that he knew how to have fun and could look after himself.

Luke, with his effectively stylish and apparently imposing exterior, was in fact the well-bred son of

Bernard McAllister, the very middle-class doctor of Emmerdale and his attractive wife Angharad, who taught at the local school.

He was there with his mate, Biff, who posed a rougher, but equally well-mannered, foil to his girlfriend Jessica, Luke's pretty, auburn-haired sister. All three were doing a good job to keep an interesting gloss on the proceedings ... until the supercool, Neanderthal presence of outsider Ben Dingle, cruised past them without paying.

Ben Dingle had a big opinion of himself. That was clear. And when he went over to Vic's car and helped himself and his mates to a clutch of drinks, again without paying, he showed himself capable of some basic verbal footwork, disarming the Cockney when he objected to Ben's behaviour, by asking to see Vic's vendor licence.

Ben then began further to stamp his presence on the party by racing around Pollard's field in his car, coming painfully close to injuring other kids as they scattered in front of him.

Something had to be done, the problem was who was up to doing it. The job fell spontaneously to Dave Glover. Another new recruit to the recently burgeoning brat pack in Emmerdale, Dave presented a rather more boyish and smiling, but no less smouldering countenance than Luke's, and was much more natural and adventurous.

He had just arrived in the village with his parents, Ned and Jan Glover, his striking sister Linda, and younger brother Roy, after their farm on the other side of Robbelsfield had been sold under them by a pension fund.

Ned and Jan Glover had known the Sugdens for years. They were hewn from similar stock. Ned was principled and tough, Jan, hardworking, loyal and friendly. They'd hit hard times, but didn't bleat. Ned had simply packed the family into his caravan, which he'd won at a bare-knuckle boxing contest, and gone in search of work. Ned had had quite a name as a boxer in the area as a young man and still did 'a bit of arm wrestling just for fun,' as he informed Jack when he parked his van outside Hawthorn Cottage and asked whether he could give him

Left: Luke and Jessica, the stylishly groomed, middle-class children of Bernard and Angharad McAllister, were about to discover that they were no match for outsider Ben Dingle.

Tough, hardworking Ned Glover brought his wife Jan, sons Dave and Roy and their striking daughter Linda to Emmerdale in the caravan which Ned had won with prize money from bare knuckle boxing.

any work. Jack would see him alright until he got on his feet.

So the family had stayed in Emmerdale, and now Ned's son, Dave, had decided to call Ben Dingle's bluff. He stood in the path of the car, daring Ben to run him down. Joe Sugden, who had not yet left for Spain, had come down to complain about the noise. He was the only one present who knew enough

about the Dingles to know, too, that Ben would not bottle out. At the last minute Joe threw himself at Dave, pushing him out of the car's path, in the process busting his ankle and hurting Dave badly enough to disable him as Ben Dingle's car screeched to a halt.

Ben got out and was immediately attacked by Jessica, her little fists pummelling his chest. Evidently enjoying every minute of her attentions, Ben bent down, buried his head in Jessica's fulsome hair and stuck his tongue in her ear. Biff took a swing at him, missed and was then floored by Ben before the Neanderthal set about Luke.

It was immediately apparent that Luke, for all his looks and leather, was no fighter. Forced against the boot of Ben's car, it was all he could do to protect his precious features from Ben's well-drilled fists.

What a surprise, then, when, suddenly, Ben rolled out of a clinch with a bloody nose and fell unconscious to the ground.

It was immediately apparent that Luke, for all his looks and leather, was no match for Ben Dingle.

The arrival of the Dingles brought mayhem to Emmerdale. They were not social animals but outcasts and predators. Joe hadn't seen 'hide nor hair of them for years,' even though they'd been squatting in a pigsty of a place next to old Holdgate's house on the edge of the Home Farm Estate for nigh on thirty years. Now the fight at Pollard's field gave them the best excuse to prey on the community from within. For Ben Dingle died from the blow which Luke McAllister dealt him. That was the way the Dingles saw it, and the post-mortem backed them. As far as the Dingles were concerned Emmerdale owed them a debt. 'Creditor' was an unusual position for the Dingles to occupy, and they milked it for all they were worth.

The family were criminals first and foremost. Kim Tate would later describe one of them as an 'in-bred walking crime statistic'. Zak Dingle, the father, was a

Zak, Nellie, Sam, Tina and Butch. The Dingles' ferocity was a mark of their outcast status. They were the underclass, the forgotten people, and their morality flowed from that. Society was fair game.

burly bruff man, and a sometime prize fist fighter like Ned Glover. Had he ever teamed up with Eric Pollard on a scam (so far he hasn't, though both his other sons, Butch and Sam have) he might have cut a sort of Bill Sykes figure to Eric Pollard's Gentleman Fagin. But for all Zak's tough exterior, he deferred to his wife, Nellie, in the home. Zak's love for Nellie came with deep respect – he had even named one of his pigs after her. 'I don't know what she does to the enemy,' he once said, 'but she terrifies me.'

Nellie was a scream. Quite literally. She had a voice that could strip paint at 20 metres. And she was tough like Zak. She would think nothing of throwing a bucket of slurry over Frank Tate when he turned up to root them out. But Nellie was also a mother, in the family sense. Family was important to both her and Zak. They cared, even if the Dingle idea of family was something of a parody of Annie's.

Nellie ruled the roost with an iron fist, while Zak could be proud of Sam when he thought he was trying to break into Eric Pollard's place, and he could be proud of both the boys when they suggested robbing Holdgate's farmhouse next door after the old man had died. The Dingles belonged to the underclass, the forgotten people, and their morality flowed from that. Society was fair game.

When Ben Dingle died, Luke McAllister was taken into custody. It was a cruel blow for a well-bred middle-class kid with little sense of the real world, and Luke was scared out of his wits, certain that he would never get out. Fortunately he had a father who believed in him, or at least believed that he wasn't up to felling a lad like Ben Dingle.

A second post-mortem would show that Ben's death was due to a medical condition. But by then the Dingles had developed a taste for life in the community, and would not be deterred by such a reversal. The Establishment never backs families like the Dingles. In the big wide world, they are the threat. It wouldn't have come as a surprise to the family that the medics had changed their mind.

During the sword dance at Open Day at Frank Tate's Heritage Farm (Elizabeth Feldmann's old place, Blackthorn Farm), Butch Dingle, a stocky ginner who, if fit, might have made a useful prop forward for the Bradford Bulls or at least Ryedale York, emerged from the crowd and made it clear where the Dingles stood.

'There's a score to be settled,' he warned, and later at the swings in the village he appeared again before Jessica and Biff with a bunch of his cronies and told Jessica to make sure that Luke got the message in prison that he'd not look so pretty if he ever got out.

Inevitably there was a fight between Ned Glover and Zak Dingle, fired by the hostility. The two ex-pros engaged like a couple of thick-skinned old rhinos in the mud. Eventually Ned won, but it settled nothing, other than further to establish the Dingles presence in the life of Emmerdale.

Zak and Nellie had a daughter, too, Tina Marie. On

Ned Glover and Zak Dingle, the two ex-pros engaged like a couple of thick-skinned rhinos in the mud.

Tina, a short but well-proportioned brunette with a challenging sensuality and a natural intelligence, which turned deviousness into an art form.

the surface she was as hard as nails, and much more intelligent and devious than her two brothers. She once said of Sam, 'While you're around, I'll always be the clever one in the family and the dog comes second.'.

A small but well-proportioned brunette with a challenging sensuality, Tina had been expelled from her last school for assaulting a teacher. A village barn dance on the day of the memorial service for the plane crash was her first opportunity to strutt her stuff in Emmerdale. Her eyes settled receptively on a dish of a lad with long blond locks and they began to dance.

It looked like a promising flirtation until her brother, Butch, grabbed her and demanded, 'Why are you dancing with your brother's murderer?', and Tina reeled round and spat in Luke's face.

Luke McAllister, fresh out of prison, retreated, but Tina wouldn't let the incident go. First she began picking on his sister, Jessica, at school, and accused Luke's mother, Angharad (and on a later occasion, his father, Bernard) of assaulting her, working her own hot little finger into the Head Master's psyche in the process, so that he took Tina's side.

When life for Angharad as a teacher at Emmerdale's school was made unbearable by Tina, she left, and pretty soon both she and her husband cleared out of Emmerdale altogether for a new practice in London, leaving their children behind rather than move Luke as he worked his way up to his A Level exams.

Then one day Luke ran into Tina in the corridor at school when there was no-one else around. For a moment, the world stood still. There was calm. The mad whirlwind stopped. And Tina knew she had him. Then the little vixen drew her finger suggestively down Luke's cheek and passed on.

Every night was party night at Luke McAllister's house, with his parents gone. Inevitably, one night Tina turned up with their mutual friend, Dolores Sharp, and just as inevitably, she turned up later on her own and came right to the point.

'I'm not a slag or a pushover,' she said, drowning Luke in the liquid sensuality of her eyes, 'but I want you.'

Next morning, Tina hit Luke with the reality of what he had done. She warned him that Butch and Sam would not take kindly to the news that they'd

The spread on the edge of the Home Farm Estate, where the Dingles had lived rent free for thirty years in some outbuildings adjacent to Holdgate's farmhouse.

Butch grabbed Tina and demanded, 'Why are you dancing with your brother's murderer?' and Tina reeled round and spat in Luke's face.

slept together, and to press home the point, she asked him if he liked hospital food. But despite himself, Luke wanted more.

Tina knew it and made a point of not calling him. Then she set about Jessica again. She arranged for her friend, Sadie, to be with Biff when she knew a visit from Jessica was imminent. Then she appeared before Biff, clothed only in a towel. It seemed an extraordinary strategy, if Luke was what she wanted, but Tina's intuition was unassailable.

Jessica confronted Luke. She told her brother how Tina was trying to break up her relationship with Biff, Luke's best friend, that it was obvious to everyone but him that Tina was trying to destroy the McAllister family.

But Luke had been stung, and like the drone who can't stop himself flying high above the hive to mate with his Queen before she cruelly strips him of his manhood, Luke was completely under Tina's spell.

Jessica knew that something drastic had to be done,

'I'm not a slag or a pushover,' Tina said, drowning-Luke in the liquid sensuality of her eyes.

and she called Tina's mother Nellie on the phone, pretending to be a friend of Tina's from school. She told Nellie where Tina had been staying at night. Zak burst into the Woolpack, looking for Tina, and then he and Butch discovered her with Luke in the village, kissing. Zak hurled himself into the attack, but was stopped in his tracks by Tina. She was pregnant, she told her dumfounded father, pregnant with Luke's child.

When Nellie heard about it, she disowned her daughter, and Zak backed her, throwing Tina out of the house.

Jessica couldn't believe that Luke still couldn't see what Tina was doing. But Tina was isolated from her family now. She even refused Zak when he turned up at Luke's and pleaded with her after all to come

Every night was party night at Luke McAllister's house (right).

When Luke went to tea with the Dingles, table talk ranged from nit nurses and headlice to pigs, and the spectre of Ben's death reared its ugly head too.

home. To Luke that was a measure of her commitment and he reaffirmed his to Tina in the only way he knew. He turned down Biff's offer of his life savings to pay for an abortion, and on May 18, 1995, he asked Tina to marry him.

Even Tina was surprised. Luke's honest depth of feeling nearly disarmed her.

But she accepted him. Was she truly hooked? Was Tina perhaps a little scared that the whole thing had been taken too far? She told her mother she was scared and Nellie, taking her to mean that she was anxious about becoming a wife and mother, softened and invited the couple round for tea. How could Nellie leave her only daughter out in the cold when she was pregnant and about to be married? It was not in Nellie's nature.

The tea was a hoot. Nellie introduced Butch as Francis, a name no-one knew, or had forgotten, he had. It was brought out like the family silver to impress Tina's middle-class catch. Table talk ranged from nit nurses and headlice to pigs, and, precisely

because Nellie was desperate that it wouldn't, Ben's death came up too.

Afterwards Zak was not happy. He described Luke as 'a fairy' and a 'daisy', but by then Nellie was as bound up with the idea of the wedding as a broody hen bent on hatching her chicks. There would be no turning back.

Jessica, by this time, had given up on her brother and announced she was leaving Emmerdale to join her parents in London. Tina was evidently pleased. It was what she had wanted. The last straw for Jessica had been Tina convincing Butch that she harboured a secret desire for him, which ended with Biff fighting Butch in the Woolpack, and Betty Eagleton pouring an ice bucket over them.

With Jessica out of the way, Tina's strategy proceeded unchecked. First she used her advancing pregnancy to ruin Luke's chances of university. Luke had been preparing to sit an A Level exam when she phoned the school complaining of stomach pains and Luke came home. Then she seized upon the wedding as a means to drain Luke's financial resources, applying for a credit card in Luke's name and selling the McAllister's grandfather clock behind Luke's back to Eric Pollard, forcing Pollard's bid up to £1,200 and demanding a receipt for half the amount, keeping £600 for herself. Then, when Luke managed to get £450 by selling his motorbike, his prize possession, Tina earmarked the money for Dolores' bridesmaid dress.

We may have long lost sympathy for Luke, but of course he didn't know the half of what was going on until it was too late. He was at the mercy of a master manipulator. All that he knew was that he loved Tina. Blind love perhaps, but there it was. All

would come right once they were married, he was sure of that.

Finally, the big day dawned. Luke made his vows and the vicar turned to Tina, 'Will you take Luke Bernard James to be your husband . . .?' and she brought the whole thing to a close.

'No!' she shouted to the stunned congregation, 'No! He's a murderer . . . I hate you with every single breath in my body!' And then, having confessed that she had never been pregnant, she walked calmly out of the church.

It was an extraordinary work of vengeance. Miss Haversham would have been proud of Tina. Not even Dickens in *Great Expectations* had Estelle reducing Pip to this. Biff and his friend, Dave, found Luke

When the big day dawned, Luke made his vows and Tina turned to him and said, 'I hate you with every single breath in my body.'

Tina's outburst stunned the congregation and then the fighting broke out.

Was there real remorse reflected in Tina's tears, even deep-down perhaps a love like Luke's, a love which her passion for revenge had eclipsed? We might want to believe it. Dickens was advised by a friend to give *Great Expectations* a happy ending rather than the sad one he had written initially, and he did so. But the story of Luke McAllister and Tina Dingle has the tragic ending only possible in real life.

There were few episodes to compare with Tina's devious manipulation of Luke in twenty years of Emmerdale's history. It wasn't sparked by any great social change, except that Emmerdale now had its underclass. It had its inspiration in Tina's fierce loyalty to her family and a primitive desire for revenge, which took her over completely. Hard emotions like this were new to the village, but very shortly they would be seen again, emanating from a very different

Was there remorse reflected in Tina's tears, even deep-down perhaps a love as strong as Luke's?

wandering in the road, crying and covered in cuts and bruises, and still insisting that Tina loved him. Maybe he was right.

In due course he would tell them that he had decided to leave Emmerdale, but he wanted to see Tina one more time. Luke found her at the Woolpack, and they drove away together in his mate Dave's van. She told Luke that she no longer hated him, but, she said, he must leave Emmerdale, the sooner the better. That was all Luke needed to know. He banged the van into action and drove at incredible speed down narrow country lanes. Tina began to panic and wrestled with her door, the speed of the van as it careered round a corner hurling her out into the road. Luke swerved and drove straight into a wall, Tina watching as he was consumed by the flames.

Privately, Tina would cry. She would cry over a picture of her and Luke together. She would even leave flowers at the scene of Luke's death and accept silently with remorse a brutal dressing down from Betty Eagleton. She would plead with Biff that she hadn't meant Luke to die.

source, but again from a woman.

Strong women were no strangers to the Dales. In times past they had had to battle and scrimp to keep their families together. But now their strength was being directed to a different end. In dramas of the heart, women are now the lead characters. They decide what happens, they direct the course of events. This was definitely something new. It had not been so in Jack's day or even Joe's.

When Rachel Hughes got fresh between the sheets with Chris Tate after his wife, Kathy, had stuck with him following the plane crash, the affair drove Kathy wild. She turned up at Dr Bernard McAllister's surgery, where Rachel was a receptionist, and in earshot of the waiting patients, she let Rachel have it. When later she caught Rachel and Chris kissing under her own roof – at Mill Cottage – she screamed for Rachel to leave the house, lunged at her and started a fight. Then, when Chris shouted at Kathy not to hurt Rachel because she was pregnant with his child, Kathy pushed him out of his wheelchair.

Like a hungry fighter without an opponent Kathy next picked on Dr McAllister. Admittedly McAllister had been a little more attentive to Kathy than to his other patients (on one occasion they had kissed), but was that enough to warrant Kathy sending red roses to his house with a card for Angharad to read? 'Bernard,' it said, 'something beautiful to reflect the moments we've spent together, your loving Kathy.' Then, at the re-marriage of Frank and Kim Tate in Ripon Cathedral, she had tried to straighten McAllister's collar and Angharad had screamed to her to 'get away from my husband and stay away.'

The women – Rachel and Kathy, and in her way Angharad – were the front runners in all this. And as if to underline the relatively insignificant part played by the men in the case, when, after all the heartache, Chris made plans to marry Rachel, she decided not to

Kathy's husband, Chris Tate, with Rachel Hughes. Their affair drove Kathy mad, almost literally.

Under landlord Alan Turner, the Woolpack got a whole new look.

New managers Terry and Britt Woods behind the bar.

The Woolpack well, a Valentine gift for Nellie, in its new position in front of the Dingles' residence.

enticed Zoe out to his place on the pretext of business and revealed the pathetic vulnerability of his own virility by attacking her sexually and suggesting to Zoe that all she needed to get back on the rails was a good seeing to.

Emma's designs brought more than a new look to the Woolpack. Turner's was an ambitious refurbishment project and he had had to turn to Monks Brewery for financial support. The brewery let it be known that they would look on the project more favourably if he employed a manager, and Turner subsequently employed a couple, Terry and Britt Woods to the position.

In the process of the refurbishment Turner had chucked the old bar furniture into a skip along with the Woolpack well, remnants of a bygone age which proved irresistible to Zak Dingle. He and Butch took them home and Zak gave Nellie the well as a Valentine Day's gift.

When the Dingles had gone, Turner was pleased to see the back of them. But his description of the clan – 'like creeping damp, once you've gottem, you've got

Zak Dingle with Alan Turner, who described the whole clan as 'like creeping damp, once you've gottem, you've got to spend all your time keeping an eye on them.'

to spend all your time keeping an eye on them' – carried more truth than he would have wished.

A week later, on the night of the official re-opening of the Woolpack, the whole family returned for an evening out. Alan Turner's celebrity guest was cricketer Ian Botham, who made a speech and drew the raffle, which Nellie won. At the end of it all, Turner had to disentangle Nellie from Ian as he tried to make his exit.

Nellie's prize (alas for Turner) was a family meal at the Woolpack. So back they came the following night and this time Nellie brought the entire Dingle clan, thirteen of them. 'It says nowt about numbers,' she assured them.

When they arrived, Turner was horrified. Zak complained that the soup was cold, Butch tried to chat up Rachel Hughes, then Britt and Tina clashed as Tina flirted with Terry.

Finally, when Alan presented the drinks bill, the Dingles payed with 10p pieces looted from their gas meter. Turner was convinced that this had to be the last meal they ate there – 'The food will be too rich for their palates,' he reassured himself. But he couldn't have been more wrong. Henceforth the Woolpack

Right: At the grand re-opening of the Woolpack, Nellie Dingle won the raffle - a family meal at the pub. She came back the following day to collect and brought the entire Dingle clan with her, thirteen of them!

was the Dingles' local.

The Dingles were now part of Emmerdale, and their absorption into the life of the place softened some of the edges of their characters and gave Emmerdale some amusement in return.

Having taken their first step into the community they were soon dreaming up enterprising schemes to become part of its economy.

Zak and Butch were planning a rat-catching business to be promoted via a megaphone from the Dingle ratmobile, as it passed through the village. Butch had caught a rat he named after Jessica and together they developed the close and tender relationship the original Jessica had refused him – 'I've only had her a day and she knows me already,' he boasted proudly. But Nellie threatened to wring its neck if he brought it into the house again.

Zak suggested that they release the rat into the Woolpack to drum up business, and he and Butch took it to the pub in a sack, Zak making a point of telling Butch to act normally. Unfortunately, Butch interpreted this to mean he should be pleasant, which was hardly normal. In fact, so unusually pleasant was he to Betty Eagleton that she suspected at once that something was up.

When they let the rat loose, it settled in Betty's

The village hall, where Eric Pollard set up shop and with Sam Dingle's assistance filled it with stolen goods.

'I've only known her a day,' Butch boasted of the rat he christened Jessica, 'and she knows me already.'

shopping basket. Zak tried in vain to get its attention, but Jessica knew when she was well off, and when Betty set off home the rat went with her. The Dingles followed in hot pursuit, but when they arrived at Betty's cottage they heard an ominous thumping noise inside and then watched as Betty dumped the rat's carcass outside.

Butch was heartbroken of course, but there was another enterprise afoot. Eric Pollard and Terry Woods were starting up an antiques auction in the village hall, and Pollard decided that Butch and Sam filled the bill as go-fers. They were certainly thick enough not to ask too many questions. But the blessing the conman saw in the Dingle brothers' lack of grey matter would not always be to his advantage.

On one occasion Eric commissioned Sam to undertake a house clearance of No. 14 Skipdale Road. Unfortunately, Sam mistook what Pollard had said

WPC Barbara Metcalfe, whom Eric Pollard invited back to his home for a nightcap.

and, while the owners were out, he and Butch cleared out No. 40 Skipdale Road instead.

Pollard, whose village hall warehouse was now full of stolen property, ordered Sam and Butch to return the furniture to No. 40 Skipdale Road immediately. His concern stemmed not from any sudden attack of conscience, but from a problem he was having in his personal life, which brought him dangerously close to the law. He had invited WPC Barbara Metcalfe back to his home for a nightcap, and Barbara had stayed for breakfast as well.

Even a decade earlier it would have seemed an extraordinary state of affairs for a known criminal to share a relationship with an officer of the law active in protecting the community from the likes of Pollard. But in a world that had tried most other stimulants, Eric found the mix a choice aphrodisiac.

First thing next morning, neighbours Betty Eagleton and Viv Windsor were intrigued by the sight of WPC Metcalfe leaving Eric's cottage. 'Is that what's known as a dawn raid?' asked Viv rather drily. Then Betty noticed a man in a car nearby, apparently watching Eric's house.

The two women kept an eye on the man for a while and then Betty took down the car's registration number, very obviously, so that the driver would notice and hopefully go away. But he didn't. Instead, he asked her what she was doing, and Betty threatened to call the police if he didn't go away. The man then told Betty that he was the police.

Had he got Eric Pollard under surveillance? Betty was convinced that he had and told Viv, 'It's about time too.'

Then, when Viv advised her husband Vic to stop hanging around Eric because he was being watched by the police, Vic told Eric. But by the time Eric looked for himself, the car had disappeared.

Betty, keen to keep abreast of the situation, and much to the policeman's irritation, had taken him a flask of tea, and even offered to take turns at surveillance if he fancied a nap.

Friendly neighbourhood watch had nothing on the attentions of Betty Eagleton. But if she and Viv thought for a moment that the security of the village was being served by the man's vigilance, they would have been sorely disabused of it had they been flies on the wall when Eric finally faced Barbara with their suspicions.

WPC Metcalfe had looked out of Eric's window at the car (which by this time had returned to its position) and was amazed to see that the man in it was her estranged husband, Harry, who had anything but the security of Emmerdale in mind.

Eric, perhaps unwisely, as he had a good deal worse to worry about in connection with the law, continued with his amorous engagement, right up to the point when Harry broke down the front door and burst into the room. Whereupon he confused the issue further by calling for the police!

Afterwards Eric was furious at what had happened, and one could see his point. It had come to something when a criminal couldn't rely on the police any more.

When Sam and Butch returned the stolen furniture to No. 40 Skipdale Road, they gave the owners a bonus in error of a valuable antique clock. Discovering their mistake, Eric sent them back to retrieve it, and for all their hard work Butch decided they should keep the clock and sell it themselves.

However, when they tried to hide the clock in the Dingle barn, Nellie demanded to know what they were up to, and, on the spur of the moment, Sam told Nellie that it was a present to her from Eric Pollard.

It was unusually quick thinking on Sam's part, but the connection between Pollard and Nellie had been fixed in his mind when earlier, at a party in the Woolpack, Nellie had grabbed hold of Eric and dragged him onto the dance floor, telling him he was a lovely mover.

Zak had looked jealously on, and Nellie had rubbed salt in the wound by telling her husband, 'Eric is a gentleman and knows how to treat a lady.' So enjoyable did she find Zak's jealous reaction that she then began openly to boast of her liaison with 'that casanova Pollard on the rampage', as Zak referred to him.

All of which focused Zak's mind wonderfully on the antique clock. What had Nellie done to earn it? Eric, unaware that his future hung in quite so delicate a balance (because of course he had no idea that Sam and Butch had given the clock to Nellie on his behalf), was astonished (and not a little unnerved) when Zak turned up and smashed the antique in front of his eyes with a sledgehammer.

But Nellie's purpose had always been more than a tease. The payoff was a permanent job for her Sam with Eric, and Eric's confusion served Nellie well when she played her trump card. She suggested to Pollard that Zak would not be pleased to learn that he had made improper advances towards her. His innocence would be no defence, Eric was sure of that, and as Zak had been bare knuckle champion of the Dales for three consecutive years, he had no hesitation in complying with Nellie's request.

Now, it seemed, even Emmerdale's resident conman bowed to the superior strategies of a woman. But they were nothing more than a low-life reflection of what was brewing up at Home Farm.

Kim and Frank had re-married on December 22, 1994. In the period between this event and their reunion after the fire, nearly a year earlier, Frank had suffered a heart attack while out driving with his wife and daughter following the Open Day at his Heritage Farm. Out of necessity, Kim had taken over the reins of the business, and she found she enjoyed it. So much so that when they returned from honeymoon and Frank made it clear that he wanted back in, Kim was devastated.

At first she took it out on Chris, who, in Kim and Frank's absence, had sacked Dave Glover as gamekeeper and, under the influence of Rachel, banned the

*The man told Betty Eagleton that he **was** the police.*

hunt. Chris's motive for sacking Dave had been that Dave was having an affair with Kathy, his estranged wife, which had nothing to do with the business as far as Kim was concerned. Dave was soon back on the payroll, this time as farm manager. But Kim was even more annoyed when the president of the hunt, Sir Thomas Weir, refused to re-consider stabling his horses at Home Farm.

Then, with her executive wings clipped, Kim began to regain control by pressing Zoe to part with some of her shares in Tate Holdings. She reasoned with Zoe that by becoming more part of the business she could get closer to Frank. Zoe accepted Kim at face value, and as she was about to move into the old forge she realised she could do with the £30,000 Kim was offering her. But then, when Zoe and Emma decided to buy the Smithy together, she told Kim she no longer needed to convert the shares.

Kim went next to Kathy and offered to buy any shares she might be offered by Chris in the inevitable divorce settlement following his affair with Rachel, this time making believe that her offer was made out of friendship.

When Kathy was offered £80,000 as settlement she surprised everyone by saying that it was nowhere near enough. She had got inside information on the profits from Tate Holdings, of which Chris owned one third. The property alone was valued at £2.3m, the new golf course at £850,000, the Holiday Park profits at more than £200,000, and then there were the farms. Both Frank and Chris were astonished that Kathy knew so much. She told Frank she wouldn't settle for less than £250,000.

But this was Frank she was dealing with, no easy pushover. He offered her £120,000, and she was on the point of agreeing when Kim told her, for every thousand 'he creams off you' it's another £1,000 for

The old school buildings by the church, which in spite of Frank's plans became Kathy Tate's Old School Tea Rooms.

Chris and Rachel!

On May 18, 1995, Kathy accepted Frank's offer of £120,000, and Kim was furious that she hadn't asked for payment in shares. Kathy used her new wealth to buy the old school buildings by the church in Emmerdale and open what became the Old School Tea Rooms, now a popular venue in the village. But even that hadn't come easy to poor Kathy. Her boyfriend Dave Glover had advised her to go for it, while simultaneously advising his boss Frank Tate against his interest in the place.

When Frank heard what was going on he gazumped Kathy by offering £10,000 more than her bid. But so complex had become the web of self-

interest among the Tates that fate did finally bestow on Kathy what she wanted. Chris persuaded his father to concede the sale because otherwise Kathy would have to continue living in their old home, Mill Cottage, which meant that he and Rachel would not be able to live there and their marriage would have to be postponed. If Frank didn't act, he would find himself with an illegitimate grandchild on his hands.

The episode highlighted the extraordinary way in which the Tates managed to maintain their equilibrium as a family while at the same time apparently embracing an ideal of self-interest among its members. It was something of a model for the whole village, which once had turned on Sam Pearson's ideal of the good of the whole community, and in the modern context possibly more successful.

In this atmosphere Kim's strategy to increase her influence through her shareholding in Tate Holdings might be expected to proceed without too much interference, as long as her interest didn't damage the wider family interest.

But that, as Chris alone began to fear, was what was happening. As Chris saw it, Kim had initiated a predatory strategy back in 1993 by demanding alimony in the form of shares in the company. She had then developed it, gaining a measure of executive control, by organising their reunion after the crash in 1994. Now, an emotional dimension was added to the situation, which further fed Chris's opposition to her plans.

Kim had taken a fancy to Dave Glover.

Meanwhile, Frank found himself involved with the Dingles, who lived in an old farm building adjacent to the main farmhouse of a property which had belonged to a farmer called Holdgate. A tenant of Home Farm, Holdgate had sublet to the Dingles on a rent-free arrangement, but had recently died. Frank wanted the Dingles out so that he could put in a new tenant on proper terms in a completely vacant property. Kim had it in mind for newly appointed Estate Manager Dave's family, the Glovers.

Frank gave the Dingles four weeks to get out. Zak tried to reason with him but couldn't produce a rent book and clearly had no leg to stand on legally. When Nellie saw that Frank was adamant she threw a bucket of slurry over him and Frank reduced the

The farmhouse next to the Dingles, which was now earmarked for the Glovers.

notice period to two weeks.

Inevitably the Dingles began to look for support in their newfound local community. And in Eric Pollard, who held no brief for the Tates, they found the ideal champion of their cause. Much to Chris's annoyance, his idealist wife Rachel split ranks and joined the Dingles too. And then others followed.

What bound the village behind the Dingles was a sense of fair play against the overwheening power of the Tates. The Dingles had been ensconced at Holdgate's for thirty years. Frank wanted them out for his own self-interested reasons.

At a special meeting convened by Pollard in the village hall, Frank identified Home Farm's interest with the interest of the whole community. Expansion

The Dingles' pigsty of a place next door – Holdgate's house can be seen in the distance, right.

137

Sam Dingle chained to the barricade in front of the Dingles' place under siege.

could only mean prosperity for the area, any curtailment of his programme would only cause a rise in unemployment.

In reply, Pollard fired the community's concern by linking the Dingles' case to the wider problem of rural housing. Families with their roots in an area for generations were being squeezed out in the interest of holidaymakers and yuppies to the detriment of the community.

It had become an argument between expediency and tradition, which cried out for comparison with the case in the 1970s of Nellie Ratcliffe and Trevor Thatcher of NY Estates.

And yet something about it didn't seem quite right.

Were the Dingles really as much a part of Emmerdale as the old owl in the church tower, as Annie had said of Nellie?

The huge changes in the culture of Emmerdale over more than two decades would seem to favour the Tates, and yet virtually the whole of Emmerdale came out against Frank, even raising funds for the Dingles. And after a barricade confrontation with the police, Frank backed down, and the Glovers found themselves with the Dingles as neighbours.

It looked, after all, to be a victory for the old way of doing things, perhaps an optimistic sign for the community's future. But when the Dingles ran an auction to raise money for their fight, they showed their true colours. The prize lot was a mohair suit purloined from farmer Holdgate's effects, and Tina devised a scheme to ensure a big take by putting a wallet full of paper in the suit jacket lining so that when bidders examined it they might jump to the conclusion that the Dingles had overlooked hidden Holdgate booty.

Seth and Vic fell for the ruse, and Seth's bid of £40 won out, whereupon he dashed to the toilet and found he'd been conned.

By this time, absolute control of Tate Holdings had

become Kim's clear purpose, and she was getting into her stride. When Frank's heart specialist had a quiet word with her, suggesting that Frank slow down a bit, or it would be only a matter of time before he had a fatal heart attack, Kim made a point of working him hard in the stables and then in a place where she was an equally practised taskmaster . . . her bed.

From here on in, sex would figure centre stage in Kim's strategy for power, her drive for the one spurring her drive for the other, both conducted deviously in utmost secrecy.

Soon afterwards, she made her first play for Dave, crying on his shoulder and telling him that Frank didn't pay her any attention. Dave, amazed but as excited as any man would be by the approach of this beautiful, impressively mature and powerful woman, admitted that he too sometimes felt lonely.

A day or so after Kim seduced Dave, when Frank was away, she demanded Dave come round, but he told her that he couldn't, he was seeing Kathy. Just as Luke had failed to see the web he had been lured into by Tina, so now Dave failed to see who was the spider and who the fly in his relationship.

Kim decided to impress it upon him. She reminded Dave that she was his employer and he'd better do what she asked. It could have been said amusingly, but it wasn't. Kim left no doubt what she meant. She was in control. When Dave tried to retreat and end their affair, he was persuaded to stay. Kim's tactics were certainly impressive. To keep Dave on his toes, one minute she made him feel the principal object of her desire and the next she told him to get on with his work.

Chris had locked on to what was happening, but Kim knew that she had both the men in her life, Frank and Dave, where she wanted them. And she enjoyed teasing her stepson's fears. When one day Chris found Kim reorganising the office at Home Farm, she told him pointedly that Frank rarely came in. Frank had a new hobby at the scrapyard, where Des Birtenshaw was restoring an old double decker bus. It confirmed Chris's worst fears that Kim had succeeded in pushing Frank out of the office, and he began to wonder whether she was planning to ruin the whole business out of revenge. By now revelling in the excitement of her play for power, Kim assured Chris that she had

Kim makes her play for Dave Glover.

everything in hand, and patted Dave's bottom to confirm it.

The very danger of her clandestine affair with Dave brought its own kicks. When Dave was away at a conference in Leeds, he went early to his bedroom in the hotel to get away from a boring delegate, and when he opened the bedroom door, there was Kim in his bed.

Dave joined her, but then, to Kim's amusement and delight, Frank phoned Kim on her mobile. Dave joined in the fun too, until it fell clear that Frank was phoning from the hotel lobby and was on his way up to their room. Panic seized him as he realised what was going on, and he froze as there was a knock on the door. He threw a towel around himself and opened it to Frank, telling him he was just about to take a shower.

To his relief, Frank agreed to meet him in the bar later. But then his employer changed his mind and moved directly past Dave into the bedroom asking whether he could just wash down the heart pills he had to take with water from the bathroom tap. Dave was stunned, but he could do nothing to prevent Frank moving towards the bathroom, where he knew Kim to be hiding.

Seconds seemed like hours, until Frank returned. Kim had been hiding in the shower. Frank hadn't even noticed her.

The perverse thrill Kim derived from situations like this was rarely shared by Dave, and increasingly he was drawn to the idea of a quieter life with his girlfriend Kathy. This drew Kathy, Kim's sometime close friend, into the firing line. Kim warned him that he would lose his job if he ever saw Kathy instead of her. But she was always careful to offer both the carrot and the stick, as it were, and later she softened to him, promising that he would share everything with her, the house, the land, her money if only he gave up Kathy. It was an ultimatum, an unwritten contract for Dave to sign. Kim, job, and a share of the eventual riches from Home Farm . . . or Kathy.

Kim works her way back into Dave's affections after he resigned from Home Farm and proposed to Kathy.

It didn't really matter what Dave decided. Kim would get what she wanted. But, to give him his due, he opted for Kathy – he asked Kathy to marry him – while admitting to himself that 'Kim is the one who knows me best.'

Kim heard the news of Dave's engagement in the drawing room of Home Farm and promptly dropped a bottle of gin on the floor and made an excuse to leave the room. She was furious and demanded to see him. During their argument, Kim pushed him against Kathy's intercom and Kathy heard the whole thing.

Dave may have resigned his job at Home Farm, but he had not released himself from Kim's control. With the Glovers in possession of the Holdgate tenancy, Kim now had leverage over the whole family, and it wasn't long before she exercised her new power. She warned Dave she'd make them homeless if he didn't reconsider his resignation.

If Kim's affair with Dave sharpened her responses to the job in hand, namely wresting control of Tate

had a statement from Nick Bates with his lawyer and a Trust Agreement was in place to protect his wealth.

Chris was meanwhile obsessed with his own investigations.

To Rachel's horror (she would walk out on him on account of it), he was hacking into the Home Farm computer, looking for mistakes or misdemeanours by Dave with the accounts, and he turned up what looked like an attempt by Dave to hide the back rent owed by Dave's father, Ned, on Holdgate's old place.

Chris had the mentality of a tax inspector and the skin of a rhinoceros. Where Kim was concerned he had rarely been proved wrong. But when he had to deal with normal people, when finally he took over from Kim at Home Farm, his worst-side picture of them was less often justified. Sometimes, one had the impression that if his suspicions did coincide with reality, it had been wish fulfilment on his part.

But the material he had gathered on Dave wouldn't be necessary. It was now just a question of Frank picking his moment. When the moment came and he 'discovered' Kim and Dave in bed together, he was at once triumphant and desperately sad, as his questioning of Kim showed.

'Why? What have I done to make you hate me so much? You destroyed me once. I took you back. Isn't that enough?'

In blind panic, Kim seized upon Frank revealing his real feelings as a sign of his vulnerability. Unaware that he knew everything, she assured Frank that she had only slept with Dave once. Dave was astonished that, after all they had shared, she could, at the last, deny her love for him in front of Frank.

Unlike Dave, Frank knew what he was dealing with in Kim. 'Surprised that she'll ditch you to save herself?' he asked him.

Frank and Kim then got to the point. Like two spoiled children they reduced their differences to ownership of Kim's unborn child: 'It's my child and I want it,' Frank insisted. 'You can have the mother . . .,' he said to Dave, 'and if I see you again I'll shoot you.'

Later, when Kim and Dave were getting dressed alone, Dave put it to her straight – 'Why did you

deny it? Why didn't you tell him? . . . You told me you and Frank were finished. You lied to me. Everything we'd ever said, everything we'd ever done together. You just threw it away as if it was nothing.'

Her mind whirring with plans about how to redeem her position with Frank, Kim dismissed her problems with Dave: 'I said the first thing that came into my head,' she said, 'What did it matter?' and began muttering to herself, 'Got to sort this out. Just need time to think.' Then, realising that Dave may yet have a role to play in a future strategy, once she had had time to design it, 'Look at me. Of course I lied. I had to. Everything I've ever done I've done for us . . .'

'We could get married.' Dave suggested, blissfully unaware. He couldn't have said anything more preposterous.

'Fine time for a proposal,' Kim said, as she made for the bedroom door. 'Sorry Dave.'

Her first aim was to stay at Home Farm. From there she had a call on half Frank's assets, including the farm. Possession was half the battle. She knew that her pregnancy would ensure Frank didn't throw her out. 'I leave Frank when I decide it's right to leave,' she told him. 'I'm sorry if that hurts your feelings, but that's how it's got to be.'

Dave looked at her, unable to take in what he was hearing, 'I never thought I'd agree with Frank,' he managed, 'but he is right. You are a bitch.'

When Kim left him in the drive of Home Farm and ran back to the open doors of the old Hall, Dave stood there, feet splayed, like a little boy lost. Suddenly his lack of style, the absence of sophistication of this hired hand palled before the manipulative splendour of Kim, who, like the goddess of ancient mythology, seemed to embody the ultimate feminine principle – a soul-stirring beauty with all the cruelty inherent in life and death.

Having almost spat Dave out as the irrelevancy he was, Kim moved on to the meat of the challenge with extraordinary relish.

She found Frank looking at a wedding photograph and at once appealed to the potential intimacy of the scene: 'You do still love me, Frank?'

'Oh yes, I love you . . .,' Frank responded, pausing just long enough for Kim to consider that she might win him back that easily, before he faced her with her own duplicity – 'Just as you love me!'

Frank was unshakeable. Kim, with no knowledge of the lengths that Frank had gone to, to establish her infidelity, nevertheless sensed the enormity of the challenge that lay before her. As he made away in his car, Kim ran after him (not knowing that Dave was watching the whole scene from behind a tree).

'Frank, David's nothing to me!' she screamed. 'Don't leave me, I'm having your baby!'

Kim's baby was all the power she had left over Frank and Dave. But in her hands it might be enough. Kim knew her baby's value to her immediate purpose, for at this stage no-one knew for sure who was the baby's father.

Twenty-two years after Christine Sharp had driven Annie to define the difference between monetary and true value during her wooing of Joe, people, even in remote corners of the country like Emmerdale, weighed the value of almost everything in material terms. In Annie's eyes, babies were the promise of the future. Time and again in the story of Emmerdale the joy of birth balances the sadness of death. For Annie, a baby confirmed her absolute faith in life's unending round and put man's pride and self-interest in what she regarded as its proper perspective. Kim saw the value of her baby for the future, too, but in a different way. It might yet ensure hers.

Over nearly a quarter of a century in Emmerdale ideas about the value of life had changed in line with people's expectations. But one aspect remained the same. The landscape seemed to speak ever more clearly of that elemental, even spiritual dimension, which Annie knew. Whatever may occur in Emmerdale as its inhabitants find their way into the 21st century, the village can never wholly disclaim its past, nor deny its influence on what will be. For the landscape, which bears the imprint of its rural culture and history, real and imagined since the dawn of time, is the one true constant, and is at root inseparable from the spirit of its people.